Due

THE STORY
OF VARIABLE STARS

Edward Charles Pickering
(1846–1919)

Founder of American Variable Star Astronomy.

THE HARVARD BOOKS ON ASTRONOMY

Edited by

HARLOW SHAPLEY AND BART J. BOK

THE STORY

OF

VARIABLE STARS

BY LEON CAMPBELL

AND LUIGI JACCHIA

THE BLAKISTON COMPANY

Philadelphia

COPYRIGHT, 1941, BY THE BLAKISTON COMPANY

PRINTED IN U. S. A.

THE MAPLE PRESS COMPANY, YORK, PA.

CONTENTS

1
How Variables Are Found 1

2
Observing the Variables 18

3
Using the Observations 40

4
Pulsating Stars 62

5
The Red Variables 91

6
Explosive Stars 121

7
Erratic Stars 161

8
Stellar Eclipses 173

Epilogue 199

Addenda 203

Appendix 211

Index 219

1

HOW VARIABLES ARE FOUND

IN SHAKESPEARE'S WRITINGS APPEARS THE PHRASE "constant as the Northern Star." Doubtlessly the Bard of Avon was referring to the fact that Polaris, the Pole Star, maintained the even tenor of its way by remaining in one unchanging position in the sky, unlike all the other stars which appear to revolve around Polaris as the center of celestial motion. Little did Shakespeare realize that not only does Polaris have a motion all its own about the north point, but also that it changes in brightness, in color and spectrum; except for the diurnal motion, these facts were not revealed until centuries later, even to astronomers.

When we speak of variable stars we quite naturally think of those stars that are known to change in light intensity, that is, in magnitude. Such changes may, in some stars, be of very minute amount, barely perceptible to the eye; whereas in others the change in light may amount to many magnitudes, either increasing some ten thousand fold, as for some of the so-called novae or new stars, or diminishing in light to one ten-thousandth of their original brightness, as for such stars as that very peculiar variable in the Northern Crown, known as R Coronae Borealis.

1

In the early days of our acquaintance with variable stars, a change in the brightness of a star was considered as the only variable attribute of a star, but in view of the more recent developments we are now cognizant of other manifestations of variation, namely changes in spectral type, apparent diameter, color, temperature, atmosphere, and the like. A variable star, in the sense in which we refer to it, must possess at least the quality of changing brightness to be classed as such, the other features may or may not be present. A star in which only spectral changes take place may not strictly be classed as a variable, but can perhaps be called a pseudo-variable or a spectrum variable.

EARLY HISTORY

The most spectacular recorded change in the brightness of a star is probably the tremendous outburst of Tycho's Star in 1572. This star suddenly appeared in the constellation of Cassiopeia in a place where no other star had ever been seen. In the short period of a few days it increased to a brilliance far exceeding that of Venus, the brightest of our sister planets. This new star made its appearance before the advent of the telescope and at that time could not be identified with any existing star. Subsequent search in order to identify Tycho's Star as possibly a very faint telescopic object has been unavailing. It is considered probable that the star must have risen in brightness from the sixteenth magnitude, or even fainter. This change would indicate a total increase in light of at least twenty magnitudes, or to 100,000,000 times its original brightness. But more about this and other novae in the chapter on exploding stars.

The first authentic case of a star that was found to vary periodically in brightness was the star omicron (o) in the constellation of Cetus, the Whale. In August 1596 Fabricius noted the presence of a third magnitude star in that con-

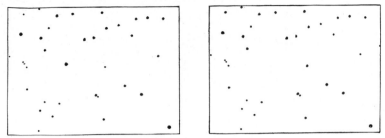

Fig. 1.—Two views of constellation of Cetus.
Left, with Mira, right without Mira.

stellation which he could not find in any star catalogue or on any atlas or globe, and which a few months later had disappeared from view. In 1603 Bayer, totally unaware that the star had been detected as variable seven years earlier, listed the star as Omicron in his atlas. It remained for Holwarda, in 1638, to note that the star became visible to the naked eye from time to time, and that in between these times, the star was invisible, even in the telescope. Telescopes of large magnification had not been constructed in 1638. It was not until 1660, though, that the star was shown to have a somewhat regular periodicity, one of eleven months.

The aspect of the constellation of Cetus, with and without the presence of Mira, is shown in Figure 1.

It was not until 1667, three-quarters of a century later, that another variable star—not counting novae—was detected. Montanari noted that the star Beta (β) in the constellation Perseus, appeared fainter on some nights than on others, and although it never faded entirely out of sight, yet there was a periodic change in brilliance which could not be accounted for by anything in our terrestrial atmosphere. β Persei proved to be a variable of quite distinct type from Mira. Whereas Mira went through its cycle of light variations in something just under a year, this star in Perseus

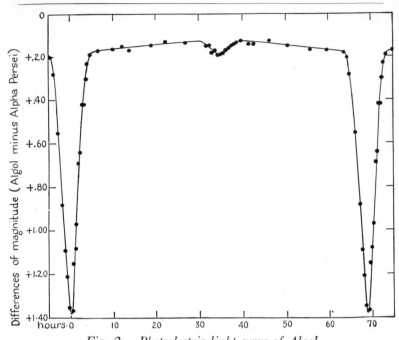

Fig. 2.—Photoelectric light curve of Algol.

Showing form of variation. (*Stebbins.*)

was faint only several hours, during every third night, but at a somewhat earlier hour on each occasion. The period of change for β Persei proved to be 2 days, 20 hours, and 49 minutes. On nights when the star was not passing through one of its faint stages, it remained practically constant as a second magnitude star.

The star is also known as Algol, the Demon Star. We do not know whether or not the Arabs, who gave the star its name originally, had noted something peculiar in its color or brightness. Its bluish color should not have given rise to the suggestion of a Demon, while a sudden fading away in light might have done so. The word Demon may, however, have had a purely mythological derivation, referring to the Head of Medusa. It remained for a young Englishman, by name Goodricke, to interpret a century later the real cause of the light variations in β Persei. He concluded, and rightly, that the fading away every three days was due to the passing of one star in front of another, thus producing a stellar eclipse. This phenomenon is illustrated in the light curve shown in Figure 2; where the fading away and the resumption of full light is shown by the dip in the curve. The two stars of Algol belong together; in other words they comprise a binary system. Stars of this class, presenting light variations similar to those of β Persei, are known as Algol-variables.

FURTHER DISCOVERIES

During the hundred years following the discovery of Algol as a variable star, only two new variables were found, the star Chi (χ) Cygni, by Kirch in 1686, and one in Hydra, later named R Hydrae, by Maraldi in 1704. Both of these stars proved to be of the same type of variation as Mira, but with considerably longer periods, or cycles, thirteen and one half months for χ Cygni, and seventeen months for R Hydrae.

The star χ Cygni has nearly twice the magnitude range of Mira, i.e. about ten magnitudes at times. Curiously enough, R Hydrae has shortened the time between recurrences of maxima by three months since its discovery over two centuries ago.

In the early 1780's four more variables were detected: one, R Leonis, a long-period variable having many similarities to Mira; another eclipsing binary, Beta (β) Lyrae; and two others, Delta (δ) Cephei and Eta (η) Aquilae, which have still another type of variation, not previously recognized. The periods of these last two stars are relatively short, five and seven days, respectively, and the ranges of variation are comparatively small, barely reaching one magnitude.

All variables that have the same characteristics as δ Cephei
have been designated Cepheids.

In 1795 three rather unusual kinds of variables were discovered; Alpha (α) Herculis, a reddish star with irregular
fluctuations of small extent, found by Sir William Herschel;
a very peculiar star in the Northern Crown, R Coronae
Borealis; and one in Scutum, known as R Scuti, which has a
semi-regular periodicity. Thus before the end of the eighteenth century, sixteen stars had been discovered to be
variable: five so-called novae, or new stars; four long-period,
or Mira, stars; two eclipsing, or Algol, stars; two Cepheids;
one irregular variable; one star of peculiar type; and one
semi-regular variable. As a matter of fact few variables have
since been found which do not, in a general way, belong to
one of these seven groups. One other type, U Geminorum,
sometimes referred to as SS Cygni-type, was not found until
the middle of the nineteenth century, but the number of
variable stars in this class is not large. The varieties of
variables were thus revealed by the early discoveries.

PHOTOGRAPHIC DETECTION

Before photography was applied to astronomical research,
relatively few new variables were found, for they were, of
necessity, discovered visually with or without telescopic aid.
With the advent of photographic technique the rate of
discovery increased with leaps and bounds. The photographic plate, with its power to gather and retain perma-
nently much more light than is possible for the retina of the
eye, is a powerful tool for discovery and subsequent study.

Once the stars have been registered on the film, we have
the means at hand for astronomical research by day as well
as by night. When we take two plates of the same region of
the sky exposed on different nights, days, weeks, or years
apart, we can compare corresponding images of stars and

detect not only novae, but those stars which have changed in brightness in the interval of time between by the plates. One excellent method of finding variables is to make a posi-

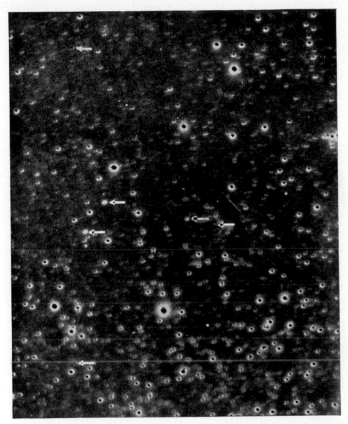

Fig. 3.—Discovery of variable stars by superposition of negatives on positives.

tive reproduction of a single negative and exactly superpose other negatives of the same region of the sky, one after the other, upon this positive. The positive will have white images on a dark background, while the negatives will have dark images on the clear backgrounds. If no change has occurred, the dark image will compare favorably with its corresponding white image.   If a change has taken place,

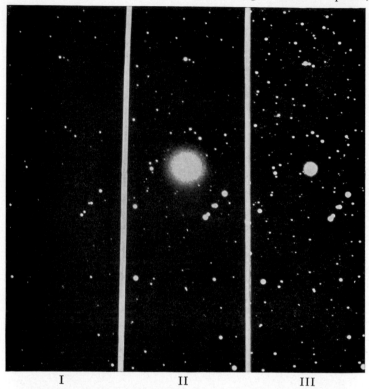

I   II   III

Fig. 4.—Three views Nova (RR) Pictoris, 1925.

I, before outburst; II, near maximum; III, after maximum.

whether large or small, either the white or the black image will be relatively smaller or larger. A glance at Figure 3 will best illustrate what is meant. Using this method many hundreds of new variables have been found since late in the nineteenth century.

The direct comparison of two negatives of the same sky-regions will also reveal differences in the sizes and density of images, if light variations have taken place. This method of detection of variables on negatives of the same region photographed with the same telescope can best be accomplished by superposing plates, but displacing one slightly with respect to the other, so that the images appear in pairs; moderate differences can be readily seen. When a bright nova occurs on one of the plates under comparison, the image often stares one in the face, so to speak, usually appearing as one of the brightest stars in the field. While it is true that most novae in their early period of eruption have been discovered first by visual observers with a keen knowledge of, and familiarity with, the constellations, many of the fainter novae have been found only on photographs, usually after the star in question had passed its maximum brilliance. The appearance of Nova Pictoris as it appeared in 1925 is illustrated in Figure 4.

MULTIPLE IMAGES

Another method of discovering variation in the stars, especially for variables which go through the course of their light changes in a few hours, such as some eclipsing binaries, is that known as the multiple image method. Here the photographic telescope is pointed to a particular region of the sky and the plate exposed for a short time, let us say five or ten minutes. The shutter is then closed for a moment, the instrument is moved in declination by a small amount, and another exposure of the same duration is made. This procedure is continued until ten or a dozen exposures are made, usually with an identifying shift between the last two exposures of twice the amount used for the others. Sometimes the plate holder is automatically shifted by a constant amount in the tail-piece of the telescope, which produces a similar effect.

The resultant photograph shows a series of multiple images for each star in the field. The stars of constant brightness will have images of about equal size and density, provided clear sky and good seeing conditions prevailed; a rapidly varying, eclipsing star will show a change in image size from large to small, from bright to faint, or vice versa. If the times of each exposure have been carefully noted, we then have the means at hand, not only for finding a variable

Fig. 5.—Illustration of multiple images.
Showing variation in one of the series of images.

star, but also for deriving a portion of the light curve during that particular "run." This method is illustrated in Figure 5.

Discovery by Spectral Appearance

Some variables, especially those of long-period and the novae, are occasionally first detected by the peculiar appearance of their spectral lines as seen on plates that have been taken with the aid of a prism placed over the main lens of the telescope. Such a prism reveals the star images as elongated bands, crossed by lines which determine the spectral class to which the star belongs. The dark lines are known as absorption, the bright ones as emission lines, and when the hydrogen lines appear strongly as emission lines in a spectral

Fig. 6.—Discovery of variables from spectral images.

Arrowed image that of long-period variable, S Carinae, showing bright lines.

image of a cool star, we usually have direct evidence for the presence of a long-period variable. A spectrum plate showing some of these significant lines is reproduced in Figure 6. The most recent instance of discovery by the appearance of the spectral lines, is that of a long-period variable found in Monoceros by Mrs. M. W. Mayall; the star proved to have the longest period of any long-period variable so far discovered; some 1300 days, twice the length of any previously known, and five times the length of an average star of this class. The characteristic lines shown in the spectrum of Nova Monocerotis were the means which first led to its detection as a nova by F. L. Whipple in December, 1939.

"BLINK" METHOD OF DISCOVERY

Still another way of detecting variability among the stars is by means of the so-called "blink" method. For this we have a machine which carries two plates of the same region, exposed some months or years apart. By a special optical contrivance, one can quickly examine alternately with the same eyepiece, corresponding stars on the two plates and thus readily detect any appreciable difference in brightness. By a "flip of the finger" we thus pick up variables in great

Fig. 7.—A perfected "Blink" machine.
Designed and constructed by J. W. Fecker, Pittsburgh, Pa.

numbers in rich fields and in globular clusters. Such a blink-machine is illustrated in Figure 7.

Another method of discovery of variables which has met with some success is the so-called "Stereoscopic" method. Here, as the name implies, the stars are projected from two similarly exposed plates into one field of view, and large or small differences in brightness between corresponding stars can be noted with comparative ease. Hoffmeister has made extensive use of this type of detector.

RATE OF DISCOVERY

As mentioned earlier, the rate of discovery of variables has been exceedingly rapid since the advent of celestial photography. Sixteen variables, including five novae, were known at the end of the eighteenth century. During the first half of the nineteenth century this number had increased to thirty-nine, and at the close of that century there were known to exist about 1050 variables, including nineteen novae. Seven of these novae had been found on the Harvard photographs. Of the 1050 variables found, only about thirteen per cent had been discovered on photographic plates. *

Quite another story can be told for the first forty years of the present century. Some idea of this rapid increase in the discovery of variables, especially by photographic methods, can be gained by the record of the discoveries made at Harvard alone.

---

* The following partial list of variables star catalogues illustrates the progress made in the discovery of variables from the latter part of the 18th Century to the present time. Many variables discovered in globular clusters, the Magellanic Clouds, and other densely populated regions have not been listed in the published catalogues. The total number of variables found to date is probably between 18,000 and 20,000.

Year	Authority	Variables
1786	Pigott	12
1844	Argelander	18
1866	Schoenfeld	119
1896	Chandler	393
1907	Cannon	1425
1920	Müller & Hartwig	2054
1930	Prager	4611
1936	Prager	6776
1941	Schneller	8445

Fig. 8.—Globular cluster, M 13, (Hercules) 60-inch reflector.
(Courtesy of Mount Wilson Observatory.)

Fig. 9.—Large Magellanic cloud.
(*Photographed at Boyden Station Harvard Observatory.*)

Harvard's first variable star discovery was made by Professor G. P. Bond in 1863 when he detected the variation of a star enmeshed in the Great Orion Nebula, not far distant from the Trapezium. This star was found in the course of a systematic examination with the "great 15-inch refractor," of the stars in that particular nebula; it was later named T Orionis. Bond subsequently found other variables or "suspected" variables in Orion, but most of them, like T Orionis itself, have proved troublesome when it comes to classification. With the discovery of a large number of variables in globular clusters by Professor S. I. Bailey, more than 700 variables had been recorded at Harvard by the end of 1901. Ten years later this number had increased to more than 3300, mainly through the efforts of Miss Leavitt who found many such stars in the Magellanic Clouds and in some rich regions of the Milky Way. Since 1910 the discovery has progressed rapidly, and in July of 1939, Harvard's 10,000th variable was detected by Miss Cannon. It is safe to say that more than half of all known variables have been found on plates at Harvard. Some idea of the obstacles that Bailey had to face in his discoveries and observations of globular cluster variables, and how diligently Miss Leavitt had to work to study the variables in the Magellanic Cloud, may be had by examining Figures 8 and 9.

Nomenclature of Variables

How do variables get their designations? This is a natural question in view of the fact that some have Greek letter names, some have capital letter designations, while others have only numbers assigned to them. The first few variables discovered were, of course, found among the naked eye stars. They were Omicron (o) Ceti, χ Cygni, β Persei, etc., and since these stars already had names, the designations were retained. When names were to be assigned to stars for which no previous designation had been given, it was necessary to invent a new system of nomenclature. Accordingly, letters of the alphabet starting with "R" and running through "Z" were assigned in order of their discovery. The letter was always followed by the genitive form of the name of the constellation in which the variable is located. Thus R Hydrae was the first to be named in the constellation of Hydra; S Leonis, the second found in Leo; T Virginis, the third in Virgo, etc. When the number of variables had increased to more than nine in a given constellation, the doubling of the letters was used, for example RR, RS, RT, etc., then SS, ST, SU, and so on to ZZ. Even this enlarged plan did not suffice for those constellations in which many variables were found and it became the custom next to go back to AA, AB, AC, . . . AZ, etc., then BB, BC, etc., through QZ, with the exception of letter combinations with J. Finally it was decided internationally, to adopt a number system to supplement the letters. QZ indicates the 334th variable in a given constellation; the next variable found is called 335 preceded by the letter V; thus V335 Ophiuchi is the name given to the 335th variable found in Ophiuchus; it happens to be a short period Cepheid.

The above nomenclature has been used for the designation of only those stars which were recognized as variable by a special commission chosen to assign such names. This commission, known as the Variable Star Commission of the Astronomische Gesellschaft, Germany, was by common consent of astronomers given the task of assigning designations to variable stars. Certain definite rules had, of necessity, to be laid down before a star was given a name by the commission, especially the rule that variability must have been confirmed by a second observer, or that conclusive evidence had been published, establishing type of variation, period, etc. Other stars, some of them indisputably variable, but for one reason or another not yet named by the commission, have been assigned provisional names or numbers. There are various provisional systems. For example, each star may be assigned a number according to the order in which it is announced as variable in a particular year. Thus 1.1939 designates the first variable found in the year 1939, which happens to be an interesting probable-nova found by Wachmann. A definite name will later be assigned to this star by the variable star commission.

Harvard gives its own current number to each variable found at the observatory; SS Cygni, discovered by Miss Wells in 1896, is H.V. 84 and β Doradus, found in 1927 is H.V. 4010. Ross 389 indicates the 389th variable found by F. E. Ross at the Yerkes Observatory. Variables in globular clusters, in the Magellanic Clouds and in the distant galaxies have with few exceptions been given no final names, but most of them have Harvard provisional numbers.

2

OBSERVING THE VARIABLES

ONCE THE EXISTENCE OF A VARIABLE STAR IS KNOWN, WE must determine its brightness at different times in order to learn the nature of its variation. If the changes are rapid, we must make frequent estimates of the brightness of the variable; only occasional estimates are necessary when the changes are slow or moderate.

MAGNITUDES

Estimates of stellar brightness are generally made in terms of "magnitude." The naked-eye stars were originally divided into six magnitude groups; the first including the brightest stars, and the sixth, those barely visible to the unaided eye under ideal observing conditions. Subsequently it became customary for observers to subdivide each magnitude generally into thirds, a difference readily discernible to the eye.

It was found later that in a range of five magnitudes there is a difference of exactly one hundred units, that is, that a first magnitude star is one hundred times as bright as one of the sixth magnitude. In other words, from one magnitude to the next fainter, a ratio of 2.5 exists. Thus a first magnitude star is 2.5 times as bright as one of second magnitude, a second, 2.5 times as bright as a third, and so on, as illustrated in Figure 10, where differences in magnitude are plotted against light intensity.

The derivation of a good magnitude scale was the subject of much discussion until a definite system was adopted. It is

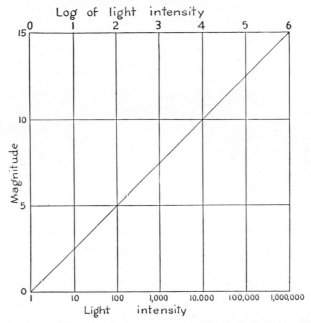

Fig. 10.—Plot of relation of magnitude to light intensity.

5 Magns. = 100 times; 10 Magns. = 10,000 times; 15 Magns. = 1,000,000 times.

based on an elaborate determination of magnitudes of the stars about the North Pole, familiarly known as the North Polar Sequence.

Accurate methods of determining stellar magnitude showed that all the stars originally called first magnitude were not alike in brightness, and so the scale was extended

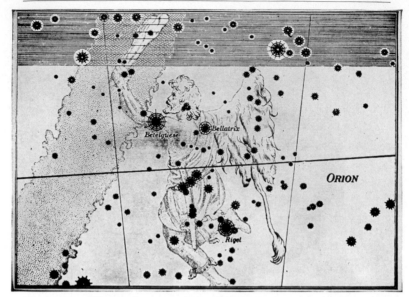

Fig. 11.—Mythical conception of constellation of Orion—The Hunter.

backwards to zero, and even to negative magnitudes. Thus Vega and Arcturus prove to be of magnitude zero, while Sirius has a designated magnitude of -1.6. This system may be carried backwards still further, and the planet Venus at times attains a magnitude of -4, the Moon, -12.6, and the Sun, -26.7. Expressed in terms of intensity, the Sun is approximately 100,000,000,000, (10^{11}) times as bright as a first magnitude star, or 10,000,000,000,000,000,000, (10^{19}), times as bright as a 21st magnitude star—one which would be photographed in a 100-inch telescope.

The first catalogue of bright stars was compiled by Ptolemy, about 138 A.D. and was based on observations made by Hipparchus about 127 B.C. The catalogue contained slightly more than a thousand stars, divided into 49 constellations. Some of the mythical figures of the constellations

are of interest, such as the "Giant Hunter," Orion, shown in
Figure 11. The brighter stars of each constellation were
represented by Greek letters, α, β, γ, δ, etc., usually, but not
invariably, assigned in order of brightness. Although Ptol-
emy did not recognize fractions of a magnitude, he did use
modifying terms to indicate stars which were slightly
brighter or fainter than the average star of that magnitude.
Ptolemy's magnitudes were used as a basis in many suc-
ceeding catalogues, particularly those of Ulugh Beigh and
Tycho Brahe. Al-Sufi, in the tenth century, revised the
magnitudes of Ptolemy to a marked degree.

Bayer, one of the next to catalogue and chart the stars,
represented them on maps instead of globes, as had been the
custom previously. He included 1300 naked-eye stars in
his catalogue and used Arabic letters to designate the
fainter stars, when the Greek letters were exhausted. Later
Flamsteed assigned numbers to the still fainter stars in each
constellation.

Numerous atlases of the naked-eye stars have been published from time to time. Particularly useful are those of
Kleine, Upton, Schurig, and in more recent years, those
of Norton and the A.A.V.S.O. These atlases contain maps of
the constellations from the North Pole to the South Pole,
conveniently arranged for amateur use and containing some
four to five thousand stars in each atlas.

It has already been mentioned that divisions intermediate
between whole magnitudes were considered necessary for a
more accurate assignment of brightnesses to the stars.
Ptolemy had used terms corresponding to "slightly brighter"
and "slightly fainter." At first only half magnitudes were
used, then thirds, which were adopted in 1843 by Argelander in his Uranometria Nova.

Further subdivisions of magnitudes, approximately to
tenths, were introduced by Argelander, and later by Schoen-

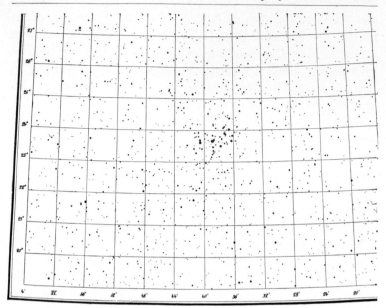

Fig. 12.—Reproduction of Argelander chart.
Showing region of the Pleiades.

feld, in the preparation of the first telescopic atlas—or
Durchmusterung—of stars to the ninth or tenth magnitude.
Argelander catalogued the stars according to right ascension
in successive one-degree zones of declination from the North
Pole (+90°) to two degrees south of the celestial equator
(−2°). Schoenfeld, using this same plan, later extended the
catalogue to twenty-three degrees south of the equator
(−23°). In these catalogues the stars were numbered consecutively in each zone from zero to twenty-four hours, and
celestial positions, as well as magnitudes to tenths, were
observed and catalogued. These catalogues were accompanied by charts or maps which greatly simplified the
identification of an observed star. The catalogues of Argelander and Schoenfeld are known, respectively, as the Bon-

ner Durchmusterung (BD) and the Schoenfeld or Südliche Durchmusterung (SD). A similar catalogue, with charts, was prepared at Cordoba, Argentina, reaching to $-52°$ declination. The magnitudes in these catalogues are all on the visual scale. Figure 12 is a reproduction of a portion of a region taken from an Argelander (BD) chart.

A photographic catalogue, known as the Cape Photographic Durchmusterung (CPD), was prepared under the direction of Kapteyn from observations made on plates of the southern sky, taken at the Cape Observatory in South Africa. The observatory at Santiago, Chile, later issued maps based on the positions of the CPD. We now have maps covering the entire sky from Pole to Pole.

Other telescopic maps have been issued in recent years, among them the Stuker Atlas, which contains stars to about the eighth magnitude, and the Beyer-Graff and Webbs Atlases, which show stars to about the same magnitude as the BD, but on a much reduced scale.

ESTIMATING THE VARIABLES

Sir William Herschel took the first step in devising means for a more accurate method of determining small differences in the brightnesses of stars, a scheme later adopted and further developed by Argelander and generally known as the "grade" or "step" method. It is described as follows by Pickering in his paper "Variable Stars of Long Period":

"The variable is compared with a known star of very nearly the same brightness, and the difference, if any, is estimated. If two stars of equal brightness are watched for a few seconds, the relative brightness will appear to vary. If one appears the brighter as often as the other, they may be assumed to be equal. If, however, one appears brighter oftener than the other does, the difference in brightness may be regarded as one grade or step. . . . When one star gen-

erally appears brighter, but sometimes the star appears
equal, the difference is two steps. If one star always seems

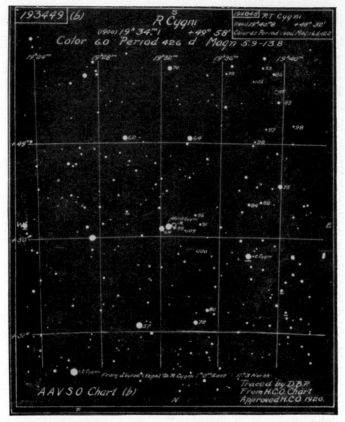

*Fig. 13.—Chart of field of R Cygni with comparison stars indicated
—type (b) chart.*

brighter than the other, while the difference always remains small, this difference may be regarded as three steps.''

This method of observing variable stars in terms of
adjacent comparison stars was in general use during the
nineteenth century. One could derive curves illustrating the

light changes which were taking place in a variable without
requiring an exact knowledge of the magnitudes of the stars

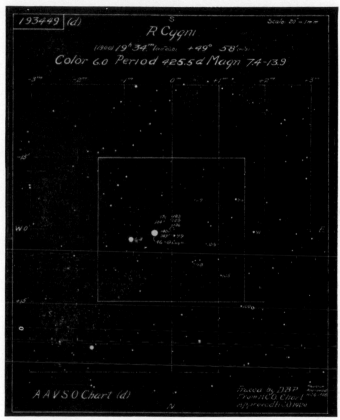

*Fig. 14.—Chart of field of R Cygni with comparison stars indicated
—type (d) chart.*

used for comparison. In the hands of the experienced observer, a grade, or step, frequently corresponded to a tenth of
a magnitude, sometimes slightly less, but more often somewhat greater.

Later, when more accurate magnitudes had been deter-mined for all of the brighter stars, and some special fainter ones, it was possible to convert grade estimates directly into magnitudes. This conversion was made possible mainly through the efforts of E. C. Pickering with the publication of his Revised Harvard Photometry and subsequent catalogues of star-magnitudes to fainter limits.

In the early nineties Pickering conceived the idea of preparing special charts for regions of variables with well-determined magnitudes of sequences of comparison stars. These magnitudes were based on the scale of the Harvard Photometry. At first the sequences were determined for a list of seventeen circumpolar variable stars, which under ordinary conditions could be observed throughout the year. Later additional sequences were provided for many stars in other parts of the sky that were of special interest to the astronomer and eventually the list included some five or six hundred variables over the whole sky. Figures 13 and 14 show two variable star charts with assigned magnitudes of comparison stars.

In the early part of the present century Father Hagen, then at Georgetown College Observatory, issued several series of charts and catalogues of variables, including many of the well known stars visible to the naked eye, as well as those observable only in telescopes. In this work he collated most of the earlier sequences published by Heiss, Arge-lander, Schoenfeld, Schmidt, and others, and brought them into a homogeneous system, supplying magnitudes based on carefully made grade estimates. Later these Hagen magni-tudes were reduced to the Harvard scale of magnitudes.

For a few years these Pickering and Hagen sequences were used quite generally for the systematic observations of varia-ble stars by the grade or step method. As long as observa-tions were relatively few in number and usually reduced and discussed by the individual making the original estimates, this method proved effective and satisfactory.

After a few years the so-called Pickering system of estimation came into vogue and has generally superseded earlier procedures. Instead of indicating the comparison stars on each chart by letter or by number such as *a, b, c,* or 1, 2, 3, etc., the actual magnitude of the comparison star was indicated, to tenths only—omitting the decimal point—beside each star so the variable could be estimated directly in terms of the magnitudes of two or three stars most comparable in brightness to the variable at that time.

This device saved further reduction, and the observer knew at once the magnitude of the variable star under observation. Usually the intervals between the comparison stars did not exceed three or four tenths of a magnitude, and in such cases it was easy to estimate the magnitude of the variable by the indirect use of the grade method, or of the "proportional" method proposed by such observers as Nijland and others. In the proportional method one gauged the brightness in tenths of the interval between the two comparison stars. Thus, if the variable appeared to be fainter than a star marked 72 ($7^m.2$) and brighter than one marked 78 ($7^m.8$) then the interval of six tenths was considered as divided into tenths or sixths, and an estimate made of the proportion. If the variable was estimated as half way between 72 and 78 then the assumed magnitude was 7.5. If three tenths of the way from 72 to 78, then the magnitude was considered as 7.4. If seven tenths of the way from the 72 to the 78, then the concluded magnitude was 7.6.

There are several ways of recording such an estimate. By the Pickering method one would record the actually estimated magnitude, such as 7.5, noting for reference the comparison stars used, such as (72) 7.5 (78). By the proportional method one would record (72) 5 Var 5 (78), or if letters were used in place of magnitude number, d 5 Var 5 e. If the grade or step method was used and the observer decided that "d"—the 72 star—was slightly brighter than the variable and that the variable was always seen slightly

OBSERVATIONS OF VARIABLE STARS

For the Month of......January...1939

OBSERVER,............John L. Doe............ TIME USED, Eastern Standard

ADDRESS,............Skowhegan, Maine............ INSTRUMENT, 5-inch refractor

DESIGNATION	VARIABLE	JUL. DAY AND DEC.	MAGN.	DESIGNATION	VARIABLE	JUL. DAY AND DEC.	MAGN.
001755	T Cas	2429420.5	9.4	163172	R UMi	2429420.6	11.0
"	" "	9432.5	9.0	"	" "	9432.6	11.2
"	" "	9440.5	9.0	180445	Nova Her	9420.8	10.7
005840	RX And	9422.6	11.8	"	" "	9428.8	10.8
"	" "	9424.7	11.7	184205	R Sct	9420.8	5.5
"	" "	9428.6	12.0	"	" "	9428.8	5.7
"	" "	9431.7	12.0	193449	R Cyg	9428.5	8.2
060450	X Aur	9420.6	9.1	"	" "	9438.5	8.6
"	" "	9432.6	9.9	210868	T Cep	9432.6	6.6
"	" "	9440.6	10.5	"	" "	9440.6	6.8
074922	U Gem	9420.5	14.0	230110	R Peg	9432.6	8.0
"	" "	9424.5	13.9	"	" "	9438.6	8.4
"	" "	9428.5	11.0				
"	" "	9431.5	9.1				
081112	R Cnc	9420.6	11.0				
"	" "	9428.6	11.4				
094211	R Leo	9420.7	9.1				
"	" "	9428.7	9.4				
103769	R UMa	9424.7	10.2				
"	" "	9428.7	10.4				
"	" "	9440.7	10.9				
154428	R CrB	9420.8	6.0				
"	" "	9424.8	6.0				
"	" "	9428.8	6.1				
"	" "	9432.8	5.9				
"	" "	9436.8	6.0				

This record, if intended for use in monthly predictions, should be returned by the fifteenth of the month to HARVARD COLLEGE OBSERVATORY, CAMBRIDGE, MASS., U. S. A.

Fig. 15.—Typical variable star report.

brighter than "e"—the 78 star—the record would read either d 3 Var 3 e or (72) 3 Var 3 (78), the resulting magnitude being 7.5 in any case.

Of course the date and time of observation had to be recorded along with the estimated magnitude; to the nearest minute if the star was varying rapidly or to the nearest five minutes for the slowly varying stars. For recording the time, astronomers prefer, eventually at least, to make use of the Julian date and decimal of a day, the latter to tenths or to ten-thousandths, as the case requires. The Julian Day Calendar was introduced by Joseph Scaliger in 1582—named in honor of his father Julius Scaliger—and numbers the days consecutively, instead of by years, months, and days, from the beginning of the Julian Era, 4713 B.C. On January 1, 1950 a total of 2,433,283 days will have elapsed. The Julian Day table for determining intervals of time between observations is in general use among variable star observers. The decimal fractions of the day are figured from Greenwich mean noon (see tables in Appendix). A sample form of variable star report is shown in Figure 15.

INSTRUMENTS

If the variable is too faint to be observed with the naked eye, recourse must be had to some optical means of viewing the star. Sometimes a pair of good binoculars will suffice to observe stars just below the naked-eye limit of visibility. Such an instrument should enable one to follow the variables until they are fainter than the eighth magnitude. As the stars become still fainter larger telescopes should be used. For stars to the eleventh magnitude a good 3-inch refractor is advisable, a 4-inch will take care of stars to the twelfth magnitude, and a 5-inch telescope should enable the observer to follow the variations to about the thirteenth magnitude. Still larger instruments must be used for extremely faint stars.

There is a difference of opinion about the relative advantages of refractors over reflectors in variable star observing. As a rule a slightly larger-sized reflector than refractor is required to observe stars to the same limit of brightness. This

Fig. 16.—An amateur-made reflector used in the observations of variable stars.

(*Courtesy of F. E. Ellis.*)

may apply more to home-made reflectors than to those made by professional telescope makers. To be sure, the reflector disposes of the color difficulties often found in a refractor, and is preferred for observing stars near the zenith. Figures

Fig. 17.—Typical refracting telescope.
(*Courtesy of H. M. Harris.*)

16 and 17 illustrate types of reflectors and refractors used by amateurs.

It is somewhat of a nuisance to keep the reflector in proper adjustment and the reflecting surfaces up to the highest point of efficiency. A refractor requires much less care, but here again familiarity with the instrument at hand and a determination to get the most done with the available tools counts the most. "The boy with the bent pin catches the most fish" often applies to telescopes of any type, size, or make.

VARIABLE STAR OBSERVERS

During the last forty years numerous groups of observers have been formed for the sole purpose of systematically following some of the easily observed and interesting variable stars. The first large group to be formed for this special

Fig. 18.—Wm. Tyler Olcott, 1873–1936.
Co-founder and 1st Secretary of the A.A.V.S.O.

purpose was the Variable Star Section of the British Astronomical Association in England, in the early nineties. Their ranks have included some very expert amateur observers not only in England but also on the Continent. Their work was made possible in great part by Pickering's efforts to supply sequences of comparison stars with which to observe variables, and later by the Hagen charts and sequences. In 1911 a group of American observers, some of whom had been contributing observations semi-regularly to Harvard, formed the American Association of Variable Star Observers, which

Fig. 19.—Typical gathering at an American Association of Variable Stars Observers' meeting.

at present has a membership of professionals and amateurs the world over. In the past thirty years this group of observers has faithfully and persistently followed the caprices of some five-hundred or more variable stars. Consequently they now have accumulated more than three-quarters of a million observations. Other countries have since formed similar variable star observing groups; notably France, Denmark, Japan, New Zealand, and Russia. The observations have appeared in printed form, generally in the reports of the organizations or in other astronomical publications, thus making them available, with more or less promptness, for discussion by professional astronomers.

The observations themselves are not difficult, no expert astronomical or mathematical knowledge is required and the results attained attest to the great value of the work. A moderate size telescope, suitable charts, and a determination to succeed are the main requirements. In fact, this sort of observing is admirably suited to the amateur and is the one field in which success as an observer can be attained with a fair amount of perseverance.

The American Association of Variable Star Observers, known as the A.A.V.S.O., supplies complete instructions for

the beginner, with sample charts and blanks for reporting
the observations.* A group of A.A.V.S.O. members is
shown in Figure 19.

PHOTOMETRIC METHODS

The observing methods described so far have dealt with
simple eye-estimates of magnitude, with and without telescopic aid. Experience has shown that the degree of accuracy attainable by ordinary visual methods suffices for
following the variations of stars with a large range in magnitude, or for which generalities about the form of the light
curve and time of maximum and minimum are desired, or
when we are watching for sudden increases and decreases in
light.

If we wish to study slight variations in magnitude with a
high degree of accuracy, then instrumental means of determining differences in magnitude are required. For this
purpose a photometer is essential, especially one which can
eliminate personal equation and instrumental difficulties.

An early type of photometer introduced the principle of
extinguishing the light of a given star, either variable or
non-variable, by means of a graduated wedge. The observer
records the point on the scale where the light of the star is
just made to disappear. The main difficulty with this type of
wedge photometer was that the place of extinction de-
pended, to a great extent, on the "sky" and "seeing" conditions as well as the keenness and alertness of the eye. If
the seeing were poor, the sky not uniformly clear and transparent, or the eye fatigued, the measures were susceptible
to much uncertainty and even actual error. A photometer
which depends on equalization of two star images instead

---

* Address the A.A.V.S.O., Harvard College Observatory, Cambridge,
Massachusetts.

of on the point of extinction, is vastly more reliable and therefore much more accurate.

A photometer in which a wedge is used as an equalizer is decidedly to be preferred. The wedge can be used satisfactorily if it is passed through only one half of the field of view of the telescope, so that the brighter star—variable or comparison star—may be dimmed to equal the brightness of the fainter star. Polaroid has recently come into use as a means of equalizing star images and bids fair to be productive of worthwhile results.

The types of photometer just described are relatively easy to construct, comparatively inexpensive and are readily adaptable to the needs and equipment of the amateur observer. Zoellner and Pickering were among the first to use the principles of polarized light and equalization in their photometers. With such instruments Pickering planned and, with the help of Bailey, completed his photometric catalogue of the bright stars over the entire sky down to magnitude 7.5, and to fainter limits for special regions.

With a polarizing photometer images of two stars—one variable and the other non-variable—could be placed side by side, then by proper manipulation of the instrument, the relative positions of these images could be reversed and the necessary equalizations made. Professor O. C. Wendell, for nearly a quarter of a century, with an instrument of this type carried on measures of eclipsing stars to a degree of accuracy not previously attained. His observations, and the resultant light curves, served as the basis for much of the pioneer work done twenty-five years ago by Russell, Shapley, and others in the investigation of the theories of eclipsing stars. This same type of photometer was successfully used by the late Professor R. S. Dugan and his colleagues at Princeton, who have determined the light curves of many more eclipsing variables. The use of the polarizing photometer reduced the accidental errors of observations to much less than one tenth of a magnitude.

The adaptation of photoelectric methods in the determination of small differences in the light of stars has brought about a still greater degree of accuracy and has enabled observers to measure to within a single hundredth of a magnitude. Also, with such an instrument, stars never before suspected of variability were found to undergo very small changes in light, and light curves, previously considered to be perfectly regular, have been found to present well-marked and well-authenticated irregularities.

At this point in our discussion of observing methods and devices, mention should be made of the special problems which may arise where a high degree of accuracy is required. It is well known that observations made with refractors introduce differences due to chromatism, or color corrections, of the lens used. Such color difficulties do not appear in well-made parabolized mirrors, since the light of all colors is brought to the same focus, but the trouble can be serious in refractors, where the light is focused for certain wave lengths, usually in the yellow portion of the spectrum.

We must be on our guard against background difficulties in either type of telescope. On an average night the background of the field of view of the telescope will appear darker through a high-power than through a low-power eyepiece. The effect is very noticeable with bright moonlight and a slightly milky sky. Then the bright background assumes a bluish tinge and red stars seem brighter by contrast if viewed through a low-power eyepiece.

Red stars present special difficulties to the observer. One of the most serious is the so-called Purkyně effect. (Purkyně is also known as Purkinje in the astronomical literature.) Suppose you have two lamps, one with a blue bulb and the other with a red bulb and you judge them to be equally bright. If you were to add another blue bulb and red bulb to each lamp you would then expect to see the two lamps still equally bright. What happens, instead, is that the red lamp will seem to be brighter than the blue one. Our eye reacts differently to equal variations in blue and red light.

The Purkyně effect is especially troublesome in the observations of red variables. If the comparison stars for a red variable happen to be white, the variable may be judged to be as much as half a magnitude brighter in a six-inch telescope than when estimated with the naked eye. The best safeguard against errors arising from differences in color would be to choose comparison stars that are as red as the variable, but such red comparison stars can not readily be found.

In addition to the Purkyně effect the coloring caused by absorption in the lenses of the telescope may affect the observations. In work which requires a high degree of accuracy and where small differences in magnitude are sought, observers should be careful to record the size and type of instrument used, and the eyepiece employed.

A further difficulty presents itself because of the gradual reaction of the retina to faint red light. If one observes a faint red star, he will notice that it will appear to increase steadily in brightness during the first few seconds of observation. Different observers have different habits, and estimates of brightness may vary considerably as made by one person or another. To overcome difficulties of this sort, the observer is advised to estimate the magnitude of the variable by short, quick glances, rather than by prolonged stares. In recent years, with the adoption of this method of observing, accidental and systematic discrepancies have been considerably reduced.

Mention should be made of the different wave-lengths of light as gathered by the eye and the photographic plate.

The eye at the visual telescope sees only that portion of the spectrum which can be recorded on the retina, mainly in the yellow and extending to either side for a short distance. The photographic plate covers, in general, different portions of the spectrum.

Photographic Observations

One of the inherent difficulties encountered in visual work lies in the fact that an observation once made at a certain time, on a certain night, under certain conditions can never be repeated and accordingly never confirmed except if by chance another person was observing the same object under like conditions at the same moment. Such cannot be said of observations made on photographic plates. These records are lasting reminders of what was happening at the time when the plate was being exposed in the camera or telescope, and observations of magnitudes, positions, etc., on these plates can be repeated several times over. Given a photographic plate, properly exposed and developed, one can observe on this plate as he would at the eyepiece of a visual telescope. Variable stars can be as well observed from a plate as by the visual methods previously outlined. Estimates of brightnesses of stars in terms of not too distant comparison stars can be made rapidly and accurately, and the history of the star's activities can be studied for as many years in the past as the collection of plates at hand will allow. The photographic plate permits us to review the past history of the starry heavens, something not possible in ordinary night-to-night visual work. Observations made by direct estimates from plates have about the same degree of accuracy as those made by simple visual methods at the telescope.

Obviously one must plan a photographic study of variable stars with some forethought as to the requirements for different types of variables. It would not, of course, be advisable to photograph a star with a 90 minute period on a plate exposed for an hour or two. Then, too, we should consider how frequently the plates are to be taken. For short-period eclipsing stars the nightly interval should be much smaller than for long-period variables.

For many sorts of variable star investigations photography may eventually supersede ordinary visual methods. On the other hand there will always be a place for the visual observer—for the amateur in particular. To him will be relegated the task of keeping an "eye" on the sudden and spectacular events among the stars, especially in the prompt discovery of novae and the enigmatic "jumping up" or "falling off" of the light of certain variable stars, such as SS Cygni and R Coronae Borealis. There is much yet to be done in "observing the variables" both visually and photographically.

3

USING THE OBSERVATIONS*

ONCE THE OBSERVATIONS OF A VARIABLE STAR HAVE BEEN made, the first step in the analysis is to present the observations diagrammatically so that the light curves can be studied in detail.

Given the observed magnitudes and the times when they were made, we can plot the light curve † with the time of the observation as the horizontal coordinate, and the observed magnitude as the vertical coordinate. The scale of the plots will, of course, have to be adjusted to the rapidity of the light changes; a very open time scale for eclipsing variables, or other rapidly varying stars, and a more contracted time scale for the more slowly varying stars, such as the long-period variables and some irregular variables. For most eclipsing variables, cluster-type stars, and a majority of the Cepheids, a ratio of one tenth of a magnitude to a tenth, or a

---

* If the reader is not particularly interested in detailed methods for making use of the observations, he may pass over this chapter without serious loss.

† Light curves may be pictured as graphs similar to those kept at hospitals to record the varying temperature of a patient, or those illustrating the rise and fall of the stock market throughout the year.

few tenths, of a day is desirable. For very rapidly varying stars, a tenth of a magnitude to a hundredth of a day is frequently used. For long-period variables we usually plot one magnitude to an inch, or half-inch, against a time scale of 50 or 100 days to the inch.

THE LIGHT CURVES

For the sake of illustration, let us take the observations made on the long-period variable U Persei, which extend over several years. Since observations on this particular type of variable are usually made at varying intervals by several observers situated at different stations over the Earth, those of any one observer would not, as a rule, suffice to depict the complete light curve. But by plotting all the observations made at the various stations, we can obtain a fairly complete curve covering the time when the star was available for observation. As mentioned in the chapter on Observing the Variables, we use the Julian day calender, rather than the civil day calendar, in plotting the observations.

For the preliminary light curve, and as a check on the accordance, all the observations are first plotted as individual points (see Figure 20*A*). Sometimes the observations are very numerous at a given part of the curve, frequently with some dispersion among the observations, and in order to determine the most probable form of the curve, it is desirable to group the observations in one way or another. For stars with periods between 200 and 500 days, it has been found convenient to combine all the observations within the same ten-day interval into one mean value, and to plot these means as individual points. It is assumed, of course, that all the observations have been made on the same system of magnitudes, otherwise a reduction to one particular system would have to be made for all the observations. A smoothed light curve, made by plotting the ten-day means,

is shown in Figure 20*B*. This curve probably best represents
the light changes of the star over the years covered by the
observations.

Once the ten-day means have been plotted and a smooth
curve drawn through the points, one can obtain a fair idea of
the general form of the light curve, note any anomalous
features which may appear, determine the preliminary dates

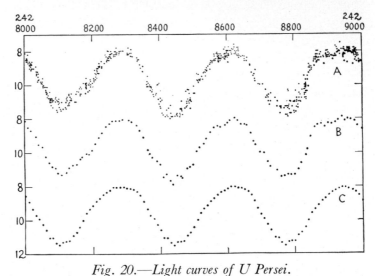

Fig. 20.—*Light curves of U Persei.*

A, Individual observations; *B*, ten-day means; *C*, mean light curve.

of maximum and minimum, as well as a tentative value of
the length of the period. A combined light curve of the several individual maxima of U Persei as observed during the
1000 day interval under discussion, is shown in the same
Figure 20*C*.

To demonstrate still more clearly the successive steps in
the formation of a light curve, let us take the observations of
another interesting long-period variable, S Ursae Majoris,
and give, in tabular form, the ten-day means which are to be

used later in forming the standard typical light curve of the star in question. Assuming that we have the individual observations listed in some published or manuscript form, we first proceed to compile the table of ten-day means by combining all the observations made in each ten-day interval, let us say from J.D. 2425865 to 5874, 5875 to 5884, etc., as shown in Table 1. The mean Julian date, rounded off, for simplicity, to the nearest ten-day value, is given in column one. The number of estimates used in this ten-day interval is given in column two, and the corresponding mean magnitude in column three. Mean magnitudes printed in heavy face type denote those which are nearest to the assumed time of minimum.

With the ten-day means at hand we can proceed to the construction of the standard light curve which will best represent the mean of all the individual cycles of variation contained in Table 1. A cycle here signifies the observed curve from one maximum to the next maximum, or one minimum to the next minimum. First, we must decide what we shall consider our zero point of reference, or zero phase. In the sense here used, zero phase is that particular point on the light curve which is taken as the origin for the time coordinate, and to which all other parts of the curve are referred.

Ordinarily one would choose the time of maximum for the zero of phase for a long-period variable, but for S Ursae Majoris the maximum of the light curve is broad and flat, and subject to irregular fluctuations which would render the determination of the exact time of maximum phase difficult. On the other hand, the minimum phase for this star is usually sharply defined and therefore its determination is much more certain. Accordingly, the time when the variable is at minimum has been assumed as the zero point to which the individual cycles are referred.

TABLE 1
TEN-DAY MEANS—S URSAE MAJORIS

Mean Jul. date	No. obs.	Mean magn.	Mean Jul. date	No. obs.	Mean magn.	Mean Jul. date	No. obs.	Mean magn.
2425870	21	8.02	2426260	9	8.60	2426650	5	10.88
5880	30	8.52	6270	17	8.57	6660	3	11.77
5890	19	8.81	6280	6	8.48	6670	..	.....
5900	9	9.07	6290	7	8.41	6680	4	11.74
5910	12	9.48	6300	10	8.21	6690	4	11.55
5920	13	10.02	6310	7	7.96	6700	2	10.25
5930	6	10.13	6320	4	7.75	6710	10	9.66
5940	9	10.74	6330	11	7.82	6720	8	8.78
5950	6	10.72	6340	8	8.00	6730	7	8.57
5960	3	11.17	6350	8	8.45	6740	24	8.38
5970	4	11.38	6360	9	8.81	6750	11	8.11
5980	7	**11.61**	6370	4	9.18	6760	13	8.08
5990	1	11.40	6380	12	9.81	6770	23	7.89
6000	14	10.77	6390	9	10.66	6780	18	7.92
6010	7	10.07	6400	10	10.82	6790	13	7.84
6020	8	9.21	6410	11	11.23	6800	16	8.02
6030	20	8.77	6420	16	11.64	6810	13	8.31
6040	21	8.54	6430	5	11.90	6820	7	8.66
6050	8	8.34	6440	5	11.90	6830	11	9.01
6060	24	8.25	6450	7	**12.39**	6840	10	9.29
6070	19	8.07	6460	4	11.85	6850	9	9.82
6080	6	7.97	6470	5	10.48	6860	12	10.27
6090	22	7.77	6480	4	10.08	6870	13	10.59
6100	22	7.86	6490	6	9.73	6880	12	11.01
6110	10	8.47	6500	11	8.92	6890	12	11.36
6120	24	8.30	6510	19	8.71	6900	14	11.49
6130	23	8.83	6520	14	8.53	6910	6	**11.38**
6140	13	9.45	6530	12	8.41	6920	14	11.16
6150	16	9.76	6540	14	8.27	6930	14	10.42
6160	12	10.29	6550	6	7.75	6940	21	9.52
6170	11	10.70	6560	16	7.97	6950	21	8.98
6180	7	11.41	6570	10	8.08	6960	15	8.67
6190	7	11.66	6580	5	8.16	6970	15	8.26
6200	5	11.98	6590	18	8.66	6980	20	8.10
6210	8	**11.79**	6600	11	8.95	6990	4	7.98
6220	11	11.75	6610	6	9.22	7000	10	7.83
6230	8	10.98	6620	16	9.79	7010	15	7.88
6240	10	10.13	6630	10	10.27	7020	4	7.90
6250	11	9.24	6640	2	10.55			

The construction of the standard light curve as compiled from the individual cycles is shown in Table 2. The first column gives the phase at ten-day intervals preceding and following the zero phase of minimum. Columns two to six inclusive, give the corresponding ten-day means of the

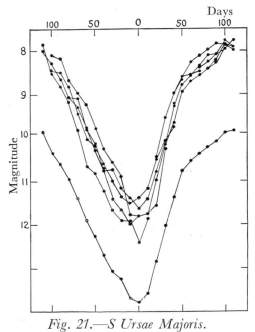

Fig. 21.—S Ursae Majoris.

Upper—individual curves; lower—mean light curve.

magnitudes for the individual cycles, found in Table 1. The Julian dates in the headings of these columns represent the times of minimum for each of the five cycles under discussion. Column seven gives the mean of the magnitudes in each cycle for that particular ten-day phase, and column eight, the average deviation of the individual ten-day mean values from the final mean value.

This procedure may require some additional explanation. What we have done here is to combine numerically the five individual cycles into one final standard light curve, and the result is the same as if we had plotted all the curves together with the dates of minimum as zero phase, and then drawn an average smooth curve through the points. Figure 21 shows the five individual cycles, and the standard curve, from column seven of Table 2.

TABLE 2

MEAN LIGHT CURVE OF S URSAE MAJORIS

Phase \ J.D. min.	25978	26206	26446	26673	26907	Mean	A.D.
−110	8.02	7.86	8.00	. . . . .	8.02	7.98	± .06
100	8.52	8.47	8.45	8.08	8.31	8.37	.14
90	8.81	8.50	8.81	8.16	8.66	8.59	.21
80	9.07	8.83	9.18	8.66	9.01	8.95	.16
70	9.48	9.45	9.81	8.95	9.29	9.39	.22
60	10.02	9.76	10.66	9.22	9.82	9.90	.36
50	10.13	10.29	10.82	9.79	10.27	10.26	.24
40	10.74	10.70	11.23	10.27	10.59	10.71	.22
30	10.72	11.41	11.64	10.55	11.01	11.07	.37
20	11.17	11.66	11.90	10.88	11.36	11.39	.32
−10	11.38	11.98	11.90	11.77	11.49	11.70	.22
0	11.61	11.79	12.39	. . . . .	11.38	11.79	.30
+10	11.40	11.75	11.85	11.74	11.16	11.58	.24
20	10.77	10.98	10.48	11.55	10.42	10.84	.34
30	10.07	10.13	10.08	10.25	9.52	10.01	.20
40	9.21	9.24	9.73	9.66	8.98	9.36	.26
50	8.77	8.60	8.92	8.78	8.67	8.75	.09
60	8.54	8.57	8.71	8.57	8.26	8.53	.11
70	8.34	8.48	8.53	8.38	8.10	8.37	.12
80	8.25	8.41	8.41	8.11	7.98	8.23	.15
90	8.07	8.21	8.27	8.08	7.83	8.09	.12
100	7.97	7.96	7.75	7.89	7.88	7.89	.06
+110	7.77	7.75	7.97	7.92	7.90	7.86	± .08

An inspection of Figure 21 shows that the best accordance of all the cycles is on the ascending branch, as the star brightens after minimum; and at maximum, when the observations are usually more numerous. The mean average deviation of all the individual curves from the standard curve—a measure of accordance—is ± 0.19, ranging from ± 0.06 to ± 0.36 magnitudes.

Deriving the Times of Maximum Phase

So far we have noted the times when the star reached maximum brightness only approximately, and by mere inspection of the individual cycles. Actually, the most exact determination is not so simple. The question as to what is to be considered as the time when a variable has attained maximum—here referred to as maximum phase—has been a mooted subject. Some astronomers have considered maximum phase as the time when the variable reached its greatest brilliance, regardless of the form of the curve, and with very little regard to the observations secured on other portions of the light curve. Frequently, such dates of maximum have been determined solely upon a single observation, with the result that there has been a wide discrepancy between dates as published by different observers. For the present we shall consider the time of maximum as the intersection of the prolongation of a line drawn through the bisection of the two branches of the light curve at equal magnitudes. In this way, observations over the greater portions of these light curves have been utilized. If these curves were symmetrical as regards the increase and decrease, and the light at maximum and minimum progressed with perfect smoothness, the determination of these phases would present little, if any, difficulty. It is when we have to deal with asymmetrical curves and peculiarities at these phases, that difficulties arise.

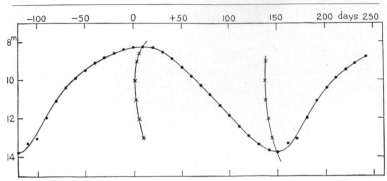

Fig. 22.—Standard light curve, bisection method, determination of maximum and minimum dates.

A convenient method of determining dates of maximum which has been devised and much used at Harvard, makes use of the observations over the whole cycle, rather than just those few at, or near, this particular phase. This procedure has been referred to as the "standard light curve" method, the standard light curve having been previously derived from a combination of several observed cycles of the same star, as described and illustrated in Table 2 and Figure 21.

With the standard light curve as a model, and with the positions of maximum and minimum located thereon, we can superpose the individually plotted curves, or the ten-day mean curves, upon our standard curve and read off the time of the desired phase. Figure 22 shows such a standard light curve with the indicated zero phases. The greatest value which can be claimed for this method can be said to be its homogeneity.

Table 3 gives, for *o* Ceti, the dates of maximum and minimum as determined by this method for the cycles observed during the years 1910 to 1940, inclusive. Column one gives the current number (N) of maximum reckoned from an

TABLE 3
OBSERVED MAXIMA AND MINIMA FOR o CETI

N	Max. mag.	J.D. max. 2400000+	Diff.	Res.	Min. mag.	J.D. min. 2400000+	Diff.	Res.
346	3.4	18874	343^d	12	9.4	19090	343^d	12
347	3.5	19217	334	03	9.4	19433	318	*13*
348	...	19551	327	*04*	8.8	19751	336	05
349	...	19878	325	*06*	9.0	20087	331	00
350	3.3	20203	330	*01*	8.9	20418	323	*08*
351	3.7	20533	327	*04*	8.8	20741	318	*13*
352	3.1	20860	324	07	...	21059	321	*10*
353	3.8	21184	326	*05*	...	21380	341	10
354	3.6	21510	351	20	...	21721	333	02
355	3.5	21861	317	*14*	...	22054	332	01
356	3.2	22178	330	*01*	9.6	22386	331	00
357	3.2	22508	314	*17*	9.5	22717	335	04
358	...	22822	350	19	9.6	23052	304	*27*
359	...	23172	310	*21*	8.6	23356	353	22
360	2.8	23482	348	17	9.2	23709	321	*10*
361	4.8	23830	323	*08*	9.2	24030	321	*10*
362	3.7	24153	334	03	9.2	24351	323	*08*
363	3.1	24487	321	*10*	...	24674	340	09
364	3.0	24808	342	11	...	25014	330	*01*
365	4.1	25150	331	00	...	25344	337	06
366	2.8	25481	329	*02*	9.5	25681	325	*06*
367	4.1	25810	340	09	9.2	26006	352	21
368	3.5	26150	330	*01*	9.3	26358	329	*02*
369	...	26480	336	05	9.3	26687	331	00
370	...	26816	326	*05*	9.2	27018	332	01
371	3.4	27142	328	*03*	9.4	27350	327	04
372	3.8	27470	333	02	9.0	27677	352	21
373	2.5	27803	346	15	9.3	28029	322	*09*
374	4.2	28149	337	06	9.0	28351	350	19
375	2.5	28486	355	24	9.4	28701	327	*04*
376	4.4	28841	327	*04*	9.4	29028	331	00
377	4.0	29168	311	*20*	9.3	29359	340	09
378	2.8	29479	341	10	9.3	29699		
379	3.8	29820						
...	3.49	(Means)	331.4	8.8	9.30	.....	331.2	8.4

arbitrarily assumed epoch, in this instance the first observed maximum of 1596. Column two gives the magnitude at maximum, and column three the Julian date of the maximum. The intervals between successive maxima (Diff.) are given in column four, and the residual, (Res.) found by subtracting from these differences the mean value of the period, is given in column five. Italics in this column indicate that the difference in days is smaller than the mean value. Columns 6 to 9 give the values for minima corresponding to the value for maxima in columns 2 to 5.

The figures in the columns of differences give us an idea as to the "period" of the star. By period, we mean the length of time required for the star to vary through one complete cycle, either from maximum to maximum, or minimum to minimum. A plot of the values in columns four and eight, as ordinate, and column one as abscissa, will indicate how smoothly the intervals between maxima and minima run. The mean average deviations are, for maximum, ± 8.8 days, and for minimum, ± 8.4 days, which is not large for a star with such a long period as that under consideration.

DERIVATION OF PERIOD

Now that we have determined the times of maximum and minimum, let us proceed to the determination of that period which will best satisfy the observations. For this purpose we shall use the data contained in Table 3, making particular use of the dates cited at the beginning and end of the table. For a quick, yet satisfactory method of obtaining the period, we subtract the sum of the first two dates of maximum, or minimum, from the sum of the last two dates, and divide this difference by the difference between the corresponding epochs (N). This is illustrated as follows:

	Max.		Min.
346	2418874	346	2419090
347	2419217	347	2419433
693	4838091	693	4838523
378	2429479	377	2429359
379	2429820	378	2429699
757	4859299	755	4859058

64	21208 = 331.4	62	20535 = 331.2

Using this method, the average period of *o* Ceti is, for maximum, 331.4 and for minimum, 331.2 days. A more exact value of the average period might be obtained by the method of least squares but, in general, this seems to be unnecessary for long-period variables.

Sometimes the plotted differences between consecutive maxima, or minima, indicate a steady progressive change in period, either a shortening or a lengthening, and at other times they even give indications of abrupt or sinuous changes. (See chapter on Red Variables.) Some astronomers have, on occasion, represented such changes in period by the so-called *O-C* curve, in which the epochs are plotted against the differences between the observed dates of maximum, or minimum, and those computed on an assumed, uniform period. For example, if *O-C* values were derived for the data given in Table 3 and plotted as indicated, the resultant curves for maximum and minimum would be those shown in the left-hand portion of Figures 23*A* and *B*. The right-hand portion of the same figure, *C* and *D*, represents the plots of the differences between

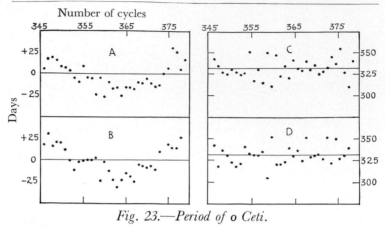

Fig. 23.—Period of o Ceti.

A, O-C curve maxima; B, O-C curve minima; C, individual cycles maxima; D, individual cycles minima.

consecutive maxima, or consecutive minima, in other words the lengths of the various cycles.

The interpretation of these two sets of curves is, at times, somewhat contradictory. These particular O-C curves give the appearance of a sinuous change in period, whereas this feature does not seem to be borne out by the "difference" curves, which instead, indicate a fairly uniform period, with frequent irregularities. The deviations from the average period are due, in part at least, to irregularities in the variations of the star itself, although some of them are also to be accounted for by uncertainties in the determination of the phases.

It would seem inadvisable to place too much dependence on the changes in period as indicated by the O-C curves, unless these changes are systematic, and frequently repeated. A plot of the O-C residuals can, however, be helpful in checking the accuracy of the assumed period and initial epoch. The general shape of the curve and the scatter about a mean value are both helpful in this connection.

For rapidly varying stars, or erratic variables which have been under close observation, one-day means are very useful. Such means have been employed in representing the variations of the U Geminorum, RR Tauri, and R Coronae Borealis-type stars. For short period eclipsing and Cepheid variables, groupings for each tenth, or even hundredth, of the period prove satisfactory.

COMBINING OBSERVATIONS OF SHORT PERIOD VARIABLES

When we observe a star, such as δ Cephei or η Aquilae, it is often difficult, and at times impossible due to observing conditions, to obtain a sufficiently complete and continuous individual light curve that will define all its essential features. In such a case observations over several, or even many, cycles must be combined to form one typified standard light curve. To do this, we must have at least a rough approximation to the period of light variation, and also assume the time of the occurrence of one maximum, or minimum, which can be considered as the principal epoch to which we are to refer all observations under discussion as the zero phase. This method of combining observations made over different cycles into one single light curve is virtually equivalent to the superposition of the separate curves, only we proceed to do it numerically, rather than graphically.

Let us take a series of photometric observations of the star U Vulpeculae as made by O. C. Wendell in 1898 and published in the Harvard Annals. The observations extend over an interval of about 100 days, and when plotted currently, according to Julian date they do not give much of an idea as to the form of the complete light curve, yet they do indicate that the approximate period is about eight days. Wendell assumed a period of exactly eight days ($8\overset{d}{.}000$) referred to J.D. 2414200.470 as the initial, or principal, epoch. A plot of these observations combined according to Wendell's period and epoch is shown in Figure 24. An examination of this curve shows that either the assumed period is incorrect, or that the initial epoch was in error. The maximum of the curve should have occurred at the zero, or eight-day, phase. The lower curve in this figure,

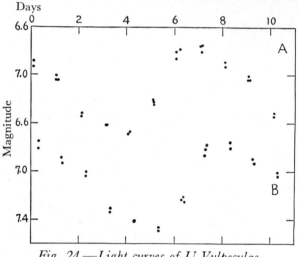

Fig. 24.—*Light curves of U Vulpeculae.*
A, Period $8^{d}000$; B, Period $7^{d}990362$.

which represents a second attempt to find the correct period, is based on the epoch, J.D. 2420400.235, and the period $7^{d}990362$. A notable shift in the phase of maximum between the two curves is readily apparent; the period of $7^{d}990362$ is evidently nearer to the true value. The list of computed dates of maxima—called the ephemeris—is given in Table 4; first for the period of $8^{d}000$ and second, for $7^{d}990362$, with the corresponding numbers of epochs of maxima which have elapsed. The negative values of epoch for the $7^{d}990362$ period are required because the observations were made many years prior to the date of the assumed, initial epoch.

TABLE 4

EPHEMERIS OF MAXIMA OF U VULPECULAE

Period $8^d.000$		Period $7^d.990362$	
Epoch	Times of maximum	Epoch	Times of maximum
42	2414536.470	−734	2414535.309
43	4544.470	733	4543.300
45	4560.470	731	4559.280
46	4568.470	729	4575.261
47	4576.470	728	4583.251
48	4584.470	727	4591.242
49	4592.470	726	4599.232
50	4600.470	724	4615.213
51	4608.470	723	4623.203
53	4624.470	−722	2414631.194
54	2414632.470		

The observations themselves are listed in Table 5; the observed Julian day and decimal, in the first column, and the observed magnitude in the second column. Phases, found by subtracting the given J.D. and Dec. from the date of the computed maximum nearest to and just preceding these dates, are given in columns four and six, as based on the two assumed periods, respectively, together with the corresponding epochs (N) in columns three and five. The phase, in this instance, may be considered as the number of days elapsed between the time of the observation and that of the previous, computed maximum.

The lower curve of Figure 24 shows that there is still a need for further corrections to the period. We note for example that the point of maximum phase still does not occur exactly at the zero, or eight, day phase on the curve.

The correction is undoubtedly small, probably of the order of $0^d.0002$, which would lengthen the assumed period of $7^d.990362$ by this amount.

TABLE 5

OBSERVATIONS OF U VULPECULAE

J.D. and Dec.	Mag.	N	Phase 8.000	N	Phase 7.990362
2414536.585	6.89	42	0.115	−734	1.276
4539.645	7.41	42	3.175	734	4.336
4541.611	7.23	42	5.141	734	6.302
4542.681	6.78	42	6.211	734	7.372
4545.641	7.04	43	1.171	733	2.341
4546.656	7.31	43	2.186	733	3.356
4547.670	7.41	43	3.200	733	4.370
4550.506	6.86	43	6.036	733	7.206
4564.546	7.49	45	4.076	731	5.266
4575.617	6.81	46	7.147	729	0.356
4576.590	6.93	47	0.120	729	1.329
4580.646	7.47	47	4.176	729	5.385
4590.544	6.81	48	6.070	728	7.293
4591.609	6.75	48	7.139	727	0.367
4597.597	7.26	49	5.127	727	6.355
4602.607	7.34	50	2.137	726	3.375
4605.632	7.25	50	5.162	726	6.400
4615.574	6.75	51	7.104	724	0.361
4625.535	7.01	53	1.065	723	2.332
4633.530	7.04	54	1.060	−722	2.336

CORRECTION FOR LIGHT-EQUATION

When we attempt to observe a particular event, let us say the time of the occurrence of an eclipse of one of Jupiter's bright moons, or for that matter the eclipse of one component of a binary system by the other, we must not forget to apply a small, though important, correction for the varying distance of the earth from the planet or star, which is known as the light-equation correction.

In 1675 Roemer, a Danish astronomer, noted that the eclipses of Jupiter's satellites showed a peculiar variation in the times of their occurrence, that is the phenomena took place either earlier or later than the scheduled times, occasionally by as much as eight minutes. Roemer correctly interpreted this discrepency as due to the time required for light to cross the orbit of the Earth in its varying positions; the light travelling at the rate of 186,000 miles per second.

The same phenomenon, of course, occurs in the timing of the light from a star, but it is of real importance only when we are dealing with rapid changes in light variations, as for rapidly varying cluster type and eclipsing variables, when minutes and even seconds must be accurately accounted for.

The amount of the light-equation correction will depend on the position of the star with respect to the plane of the Earth's orbit: it will be zero for those stars situated on the axis of the orbit, and will vary between plus and minus eight minutes for stars in its plane.

Accordingly when noting the times of stellar eclipses we must correct the geocentric time—that as observed from the Earth—to heliocentric time, as if they were observed from the Sun. Extensive tables for quickly computing the light-equation correction to be applied to any particular variable, at any time of the year have been provided by R. Prager.

KINDS OF VARIABLES

Before we take up for consideration the various types of variables it will be advisable to discuss briefly the attempts at classification which have been proposed from time to time. You will have gathered already some idea of the many varieties of variable stars which have been found and observed. You will readily note the vast differences, in form of light curve at least, which exist from type to type, yet withall, you can imagine that there are some connecting links between them.

We have mentioned that the short list of variables that was known a century ago contained most of the types which are now recognized as typical classes. The added years seem not to have brought forth many new and distinct varieties for the main types.

Numerous attempts have been made to classify variable stars. In 1881 Pickering suggested a classification that soon came into standard use. He proposed five groups or classes:

I Novae	IV Short-periods
II Long-periods	V Algols
III Irregulars	

It can be readily seen how these classes were chosen, if we recall the observed characteristics already hinted at. More recently Class I has been divided into ordinary novae and supernovae, the former those usually found in our own and the nearer galaxies, and the latter those exceptionally bright novae which have been observed, for the most part, in the distant galaxies. Pickering later divided Class II into three groups, IIa, the Mira stars, IIb, the U Geminorum or SS Cygni stars; and IIc, the R Coronae Borealis stars. In view of later information, Classes IIb, and IIc should not have been placed in the long-period class, the only excuse having been that their demarkations from normal minimum or maximum light occurred at long, rather than short, intervals of time.

Class III, Irregulars, was made a sort of a dumping ground for stars for which no seeming regularity in period

could be found. This class has more recently been subdivided in many ways by other astronomers. Several stars
that were originally in Class III have been re-assigned to
other groups.

Nijland provided three general groups:

I Regular variation
  a Algol   *d* δ Cephei
  b β Lyrae   *e* RR Lyrae
  c ζ Geminorum   *f* S Sagittae
II Semi-regular variation
  a Mira
  b U Geminorum
  c RV Tauri and η Geminorum
III Irregular variations
  a Novae
  b Other irregular variables (R Coronae Borealis
     and RX Andromedae)

Among other classifications which have been proposed is
that of Guthnick:

I Novae   V Mira
II R Coronae Borealis   VI R Sagittae
III U Geminorum   VII δ Cephei and RR
IV η Geminorum and R   Lyrae
   Scuti   VIII Eclipsing

Graff classified the variables, first according to color for
the Long-periods and Irregulars, then into Cepheids and
Eclipsing stars. He apparently was of the opinion that novae
did not belong in the sequence. His classes were as follows:

I Red stars   II Yellow stars
  a Mira   *a* U Geminorum
  b μ Cephei   *b* R Coronae Borealis

III Cepheid stars   IV Eclipsing stars
    a δ Cephei   *a* Algol
    b RR Lyrae   *b* β Lyrae

One of the most extensive classifications is that which was proposed by Ludendorff in 1928, as follows:

I Novae   VI μ Cephei
II Nova-like   VII RV Tauri
III R Coronae Borealis   VIII Long-period Cepheids
IV U Geminorum   IX Short-period Cepheids
V Mira   X Eclipsing

In their recent book, "Variable Stars," 1938, C. P. and S. Gaposchkin have classified the variables under four main headings:

A Geometrical variables; which include Eclipsing and Ellipsoidal stars, as well as stars obscured by nebulae, but not involved in them.

B The Intrinsic, or Great Sequence stars; which include Long-period, Semi-regular, Cepheid and Cluster-type stars, and the Irregular Red variables.

C The Cataclysmic variables; which include the Novae, SS Cygni, and R Coronae Borealis stars.

D Extrinsic, or Nebular variables; those involved in nebulosity.

In the Schneller Catalogue of Variable Stars for 1939 is to be found a listing of types which divides the classes into several sub-classes. There we find Cepheids, Eclipsing Binaries, Long-Periods, U Geminorum and Z Camelo-pardalis-type stars, those of the R Coronae Borealis-type, Novae, RV Tauri-type, Irregular and Semi-regular-types, Short periods, and those of Unknown types. The Cepheids have been further divided into groups characterized by δ Cephei, ζ Geminorum, and RR Lyrae.

In summarizing all the classifications, it would seem that the following grouping would suffice to include the most important types of variable stars, listed more or less in the order in which they are discussed in the following chapters.

Main classes	Sub-classes	Examples
Cepheids	β Canis Majoris Cluster Classical Semi-regular	β Cephei RR Lyrae δ Cephei RV Tauri
Long-period	Me and Se Ne and Re	Mira Ceti and R Camelopardalis R Leporis and S Camelopardalis
Red-giants	Semi-regular Irregular	V Ursae Minoris μ Cephei
Novae	Super Ordinary Recurring	S Andromedae Herculis, 1934 RS Ophiuchi
Nova-like	Z Andromedae U Geminorum Z Camelopardalis	AX Persei SS Cygni RX Andromedae
Eclipsing	Algols W Ursae Majoris β Lyrae Ellipsoidal	β Persei RR Centauri u Herculis ζ Andromedae
Erratic	Rapidly Irregular Nebular R Coronae Borealis Be Stars	RR Tauri T Orionis RY Sagittarii γ Cassiopeiae

4

PULSATING STARS

PICTURE IF YOU CAN A STAR WHICH ALTERNATELY EXPANDS and contracts. The expansions and contractions are to be accompanied by fluctuations of temperature, spectrum, and brightness. Such is the type of star we should like to present in this chapter.

Five variable stars, in addition to novae, were known in the year 1784; four of them were long-period variables and the fifth an eclipsing star. In the autumn of that year two Englishmen, Pigott and Goodricke, working together in a search for additional variables, announced the discovery of three others. One of these, Beta (β) Lyrae, proved later to be another eclipsing star, with a principal and a secondary minimum. The other two, Delta (δ) Cephei and Eta (η) Aquilae, were of a new variety and are now recognized as members of a vast family of pulsating variables which has been named "Cepheids," after the star Delta Cephei.

Delta Cephei itself pulsates between magnitudes 3.6 and 4.3 in a period of five days and nine hours. We say "pulsates" because this term describes better than any other the behavior of the fluctuations shown by the star. The rise in brightness of the star is rapid, comprising only a third of the total period. A relatively short time is spent at maximum light, while the decline in brightness proceeds smoothly and slowly to a minimum, which is usually longer and flatter than the maximum. Eta Aquilae has a somewhat longer interval between maxima—7 days and 4 hours— and shows a strong wave, or "still-stand," on the light curve from maximum down to minimum. It also has the quick rise in brightness, and a slightly greater range in magnitude. This behavior is illustrated in Figure 25.

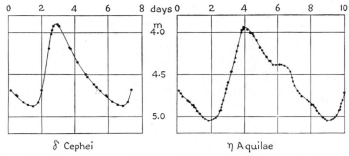

δ Cephei   η Aquilae

Fig. 25.—Photoelectric light curves of δ Cephei (Guthnick) and η Aquilae (Wylie).

The work by Pigott and Goodricke was followed by new discoveries of Cepheids, to the number of thirty-three by the year 1895. All had ranges in brightness from half a magnitude to a full magnitude, and periods between 2.5 days and 39 days. Then, in 1895, E. C. Pickering at Harvard announced that on plates taken at the Boyden Station in the high Andes at Arequipa, Peru, S. I. Bailey had detected in certain globular clusters a number of variables with Cepheid characteristics, but with extraordinarily short periods—only a fraction of a day. A closer examination of some of the brighter clusters revealed that these objects were rich mines of short period Cepheids. Within a few years hundreds of such variables had been found.

These rapidly pulsating cluster stars have light curves slightly different from those of the long-period or classical Cepheids; most of them rise with extreme rapidity to maximum, in only a tenth, or less, of the total period; and they have relatively prolonged minima, during which phase the light often remains practically unchanged for several hours. As these peculiar stars had been found only in globular clusters, they were given the name of "cluster" variables. Their longest periods did not exceed twenty hours; they seemed to belong to a distinct group—as regards length of period—quite different from the classical Cepheids.

At the beginning of the present century Mrs. W. P. Fleming at the Harvard Observatory announced the discovery of a short-period Cepheid outside a globular cluster. Its period was not different from that of a cluster variable —thirteen hours in length—and its light curve was almost identical with that of most cluster-type stars. It was at first supposed that this star, RR Lyrae, had escaped from a cluster, but as more and more such variables were found, with no probability of any connection with clusters, the idea was abandoned. As a matter of fact, the rate of discovery of short-period Cepheids outside clusters increased with remarkable rapidity, especially when photographic methods of discovery were applied to the search. Before long, this type of variable, in our own stellar system, actually outnumbered in our catalogues the classical Cepheids, in spite of the fact that the classical Cepheids were also being found in increasing numbers. Today we recognize about 350 Cepheids of long-period type in our own galaxy, with 2500 more in the Magellanic Clouds and other outside systems. The short-period Cepheids, with well determined periods, number 1500 of which more than 600 are to be found in globular clusters.

PERIODS OF CEPHEIDS

The shortest period known among Cepheids is that of CY Aquarii; it is only an hour and 28 minutes. The star fluctuates between the tenth and the eleventh magnitude, and is an easy object for rather modest telescopes. It is a really fascinating spectacle to watch it pulsate right before our eyes. When it is brightening, you can notice an appreciable variation in less than five minutes, for it takes CY Aquarii not more than a quarter of an hour to change half a magnitude in brightness.

Very few variables have periods of less than a quarter of a day. Most of the short-period Cepheids have periods between 9 and 17 hours, with a considerable crowding around 13 hours; there are very few with periods in excess of 20 hours. Only a dozen variables are known to have periods between 21 hours and two days, except in the Small Magellanic Cloud. After this gap in period-length, we pass into the realm of the classical Cepheids for which the most common period is about five days long. The longest period known among galactic Cepheids is that of SV Vulpeculae, and amounts to 45 days and 4 hours.

The lowest frequency of periods is around one day and therefore one day is usually taken as the dividing line between short-period, or cluster-type, and long-period or classical Cepheids.

Modern research has shown that the Cepheids are subject to many different rules and regulations. We shall find for them relations between period and form of light curve, period and temperature, and period and luminosity; a relation between period and radial velocity, and several other less important relations of a statistical character. All these various relations are, however, more in the nature of statistical trends than of exact laws. Cepheids are law-abiding

citizens, but they remain individuals, always reserving the
right to deviate from their own laws to some extent. They
show remarkably, but not perfectly, steady light curves;
their periods are much more nearly constant than those of
any other group of intrinsic variables, but they are not
rigorously constant. All the laws and rules mentioned above
are followed in a general way by all Cepheids, but never
with absolute precision.

CHARACTERISTICS OF THE LIGHT CURVES

Let us take, for example, the relation between period and
light curve. We have reproduced in Figure 26 some of the
best determined light curves that could be found, and
arranged them, generally, in order of increasing period.
It was shown several years ago by Ludendorff and Hertzsprung, from a similar sequence of light curves, that there
exists a marked dependence of their shapes upon the period.
For each period we find a definite pattern and this pattern
gradually changes in shape if, step by step, we proceed
from shorter toward longer periods. For example, our figure
shows for the light curve of W Geminorum, with a period of
7.9 days, a steep rise, a sharp maximum and a big hump on
the declining branch. Most Cepheids with periods not far
from eight days show similar curves, but no astronomer
would feel too much disturbed if he found a Cepheid with
exactly the same period as W Geminorum, and with a less
marked hump. The pattern system holds for other Cepheids,
but it represents far from a precise law.

Another fact emerges from an inspection of Figure 26. The
continuity in the evolution of the light curves appears to
break down at four points, corresponding to the approximate periods of 0.43, 1.2, 2.8, and 10 days. Another break
may be present around 0.2 days, but so few stars are known
with shorter periods that it is still too early to be definite on

this score. These breaks divide the sequence of Cepheids into five more or less distinct groups. The division however, is not very sharp, for as one group fades out, a new one

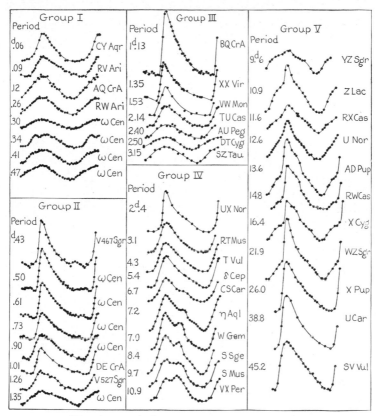

Fig. 26.—Typical light curves of Cepheids.

Note the break in shape and amplitude in proceeding from one group to the next. All amplitudes are photographic or reduced to photographic.

appears, so that the Cepheids near one of the breaks may show the characteristics of either group. As an example, we may take VX Persei, the last light curve of group IV, and Z

Lacertae, the second light curve of group V, both of which have a period of 10.9 days, but whose light curves look definitely very different.

Each of the five groups starts with few stars, grows richer as we approach the central period and then gradually fades out, as shown graphically in Figure 27, which is not, as one

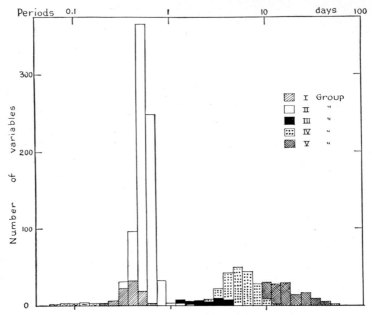

Fig. 27.—Distribution of Cepheids according to period.

may judge at first sight, a sketch of Manhattan's skyline, but a graph representing the numbers of Cepheids of successive intervals of period-length. If you simply follow the upper line, i.e., the silhouette of the houses, you will have the total number of Cepheids, irrespective of their classes; whereas the number of Cepheids within each group is indicated by areas of different shading.

The graph in Figure 27, does not include Cepheids in globular clusters or in other special stellar systems. We must also warn the reader that it does not represent by any means the real abundance of each group, since we had to select the stars for which good light curves are now available. It is evident that variables with large amplitudes, as those of group II, will have a much greater chance of being discovered and observed than those of group I with very small ranges. We may, therefore, expect that the number of known variables of group I should be much smaller than that of group II, even though they might be equally frequent in the sky. As a matter of fact, in globular clusters stars of groups I and II are found in almost the same abundance. Stars of group III, however, are definitely rare in our part of the galactic system, even when allowance is made for the smaller amplitudes for stars with periods around three days. It is this scarcity of stars in group III that causes the wide separation between the Cepheids with periods just shorter and longer than one day. If the stars in group III had been as numerous as the other groups, probably no distinction would have ever been made between short-period cluster and long-period classical Cepheids.

One of the reasons why our pattern of light curves can be considered to hold only approximately is that the light curves of all Cepheids are not perfectly steady. As an example of such unsteadiness, we may take the star AR Herculis with a period of 11 hours and 17 minutes. According to J. Balázs and L. Detre, the light curve of this star changes periodically, as shown in Figure 28, taking 31.5 days, or 67 cycles of the light variation, to return to the same shape. Quite a few Cepheids of group II show a variable light curve and it is very probable that this variation is periodic as for AR Herculis, although it has as yet been definitely proved only for three more stars (RR Lyrae, RW Draconis and

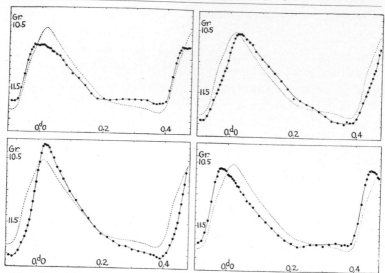

Fig. 28.—Four aspects of the light curve of AR Herculis during a cycle of 31.5 days.

The broken curve is the mean light curve of the variable. (*Balázs & Detre.*)

Y Leonis Minoris). Also some Cepheids of group I seem to have unsteady light curves. Long-period Cepheids of groups IV and V, on the contrary, seem to behave very regularly and to date not a single star among them has been definitely proved to undergo such changes.

The rhythm of the light variations, the period, is not always perfectly constant for Cepheids. In periodicity, as in the light curves, short-period Cepheids are less disciplined than their fellow Cepheids of longer periods. A typical example is that of RZ Cephei. According to Prager, this star in 1898 was pulsating with a period of $7^h 24^m 28^s.76$, and maintained the same rhythm for some years. Then, in August 1901, the period suddenly became 3.98 seconds shorter and remained at its new value for fifteen years. In

November 1916 the period abruptly increased by 4.33 seconds, and a second increase of 1.84 seconds occurred in December 1923, after which the period has remained constant to date. It may be thought that changes of the order of a few seconds in a period of more than seven hours are of no importance. But this is a mistake; a delay of a few seconds every seven hours amounts after some years to a retardation of several hours in the time of maximum or of minimum brightness.

It is not unlikely that all short-period Cepheids will prove to have changing periods, if they are studied accurately over a long interval of time. From a study of 150 short-period Cepheids in the globular cluster Omega Centauri, Martin finds that 19 of them have certainly undergone changes of period between the years 1896 and 1935. For long-period Cepheids the changes in period are not so relevant, perhaps in part because our observations are necessarily limited to a much smaller number of cycles. For the very few for which a change in period has been unmistakably recognized, this change seems to be relatively smaller than in cluster-type Cepheids.

THE PERIOD-LUMINOSITY RELATION

Cepheids are among the most useful stars in the sky. Today, whenever a Cepheid is discovered astronomers can determine its distance without much effort. The only thing they have to do is to watch the star long enough for a determination of its period; then if they know the apparent brightness of the star, they also know its distance. Here we shall briefly tell how this marvelous property of Cepheids was found and how it was successfully used to extend our knowledge of the Universe.

In the year 1912, Miss Henrietta Leavitt at the Harvard Observatory reported on the periods of 25 Cepheids in the smaller of the two brilliant star clouds of the southern hemisphere that are known as the Magellanic Clouds. The newly discovered stars had periods between two and a hundred and twenty days. When Miss Leavitt arranged them in order of increasing period, she was surprised to find that she had also, unintentionally, arranged them in order of increasing brightness. The stars that had periods around two days appeared to be of photographic magnitude 15.5 and from there on the brightness of the Cepheids gradually increased until those with the longest periods were found to be of magnitude 12.5.

Fig. 29.—Henrietta S. Leavitt.

The Small Magellanic Cloud (Figure 30) extends over only a small angular area of the sky, and we can, for practical purposes, consider all its stars as being at the same distance from us. If we make this assumption we can draw the conclusion that the observed difference in brightness among Miss Leavitt's Cepheids is due to differences in intrinsic brightness, since we can no longer invoke a difference in distance to produce that effect. Moreover, a difference in distance would not easily explain why the brightness of the Cepheids should vary in the same manner as the period. We must therefore conclude that the intrinsic brightness of a Cepheid in the Small Magellanic Cloud, whatever its actual value may be, depends directly on its period.

If such a law is valid for the Cepheids of the Small Magellanic Cloud, why should it not hold also for all other

Fig. 30.—The small Magellanic cloud.
(Photographed at the Boyden Station of the Harvard Observatory.)

Cepheids? If this were so, we may find the actual luminosities, for we would need only to determine the real brightness of a few Cepheids, even of one single Cepheid, and the intrinsic brightness of all the others would automatically be determined by our law, which relates brightness and period-length. And, if we know this absolute brightness of all Cepheids, then we can also compute what is the distance of each of them from the differences between absolute and apparent brightnesses, in the same manner that a navigating officer might tell the distance of a lighthouse if he knows its candlepower.

In 1913, immediately after the publication of Miss Leavitt's results, Hertzsprung tried to establish a scale of absolute luminosities for Cepheids, but his values were not very accurate, because of the scarcity of available data.

Even the brightest Cepheids are so far away that for not a single one of them had the distance, and thus the actual brightness, been determined with reliability. Therefore, Hertzsprung had to use statistical methods, based on the apparent motions of the Cepheids, to determine average luminosities for the group of selected variable stars.

Fig. 31.—Harlow Shapley.

Photograph by Bachrach.

In 1915 Shapley again attacked the problem with the larger and better material then available and succeeded in greatly diminishing the uncertainty of Hertzsprung's results. Miss Leavitt's preliminary period-magnitude relation for the Small Magellanic Cloud was extended by Shapley to the Cepheids of several other systems and converted into a relation between period and intrinsic luminosity, from which the luminosity of any Cepheid in the sky could be deduced with an uncertainty of about half a magnitude.

Shapley immediately realized the tremendous value of the new relation in the study of cosmic structure. The discovery of a single Cepheid in a distant stellar system, such as a globular cluster or spiral nebula, had now become sufficient for a determination of the distance of the system itself. Globular clusters contain many Cepheids and were therefore the first to receive Shapley's attention. He soon was able to publish a paper in which he outlined their distribution in space and showed that they formed a vast, flattened system whose center lay in the direction of the constellation of Sagittarius, in the region where the Milky Way had its greatest brilliance. Current estimates on the basis of Cepheid variables place the dimensions of the system of the globular clusters at more than one hundred thousand light years. The study of Cepheids revealed that the system of the globular clusters did probably outline the shape of our own great stellar system, called the system of the Milky Way or Galaxy, the island-universe composed of many billions of stars of which our Sun is one.

The Magellanic Clouds, the Large one as well as the Small, were found to lie at a distance of 90,000 light years, already outside the boundaries of our Galaxy. In 1924, Hubble discovered several Cepheids in the great spiral nebula known as the Andromeda Nebula and its distance was then fixed at about 700,000 light years. Hubble's estimate confirmed what several astronomers had already suspected: that the Andromeda Nebula is another huge island-universe, comparable in size to our own Galaxy. Cepheids were found also in other bright spiral nebulae, all of which proved to be independent galaxies, located at immense distances from us. Once a base line of one or two million light years was established from the study of Cepheids in the nearest galaxies, there was apparently nothing to stop astronomers in their new race into space. Farther and farther receded the horizon of our visible Universe; one, two, three hundred million light years, figures that can mean little to us, made their appearance in astronomical publications. The greatest distance so far measured belongs to a faint cluster of nebulae studied only with the 100-inch telescope at Mount Wilson and it reads 500 million light years.

Let us look a little closer at this famous period-luminosity relation which permitted such extraordinary exploits. As we can see from Figure 32, the curve has by no means a simple form. At its lower end, where appear the cluster-

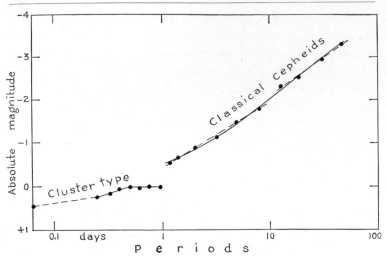

Fig. 32.—The period-luminosity relation for Cepheids.

type Cepheids, the curve runs practically horizontal, while it becomes almost a straight upward sloping line for classical Cepheids. In other words, cluster-type Cepheids have all practically the same intrinsic brightness, while the brightness increases steadily with period for classical Cepheids.

In recent times, some astronomers have begun to doubt whether the period-luminosity relation can be represented by a single continuous curve. The junction between Cluster-type and classical Cepheids looks more like a break than a smooth bridging; furthermore, Kukarkin and Parenago believe that the continuity of the slope for classical Cepheids is broken at a point corresponding to a 10-day period. If we look at Figures 26 and 27, we see that these two breaks correspond exactly to the separation between groups II-III and IV-V. This coincidence can hardly be fortuitous and there is ground for the suspicion that the period-luminosity relation may consist of as many separate segments as there are groups of Cepheids.

But let us pass over these details and proceed to another consequence of the period-luminosity relation. Some readers will have wondered why all the 33 Cepheids known in 1895 were of the classical long-period type, although we know today that the short-period Cepheids are by far the more numerous. The period-luminosity relation gives us the answer to this riddle: classical Cepheids are actually much brighter than short-period Cepheids and had therefore a much better chance of being discovered than the short-period ones, especially in the days before astronomical photography came into general use. Of the 33 classical Cepheids mentioned before, 29 are brighter than the eighth magnitude and of these 15 are naked-eye stars. As for the short-period Cepheids, even today, in spite of many discoveries, only two are known to be brighter than the eighth magnitude and neither one of these reaches naked-eye visibility.

This disproportion between classical and short-period Cepheids rapidly disappears as we proceed to the fainter stars in our Galaxy and after a certain apparent magnitude has been reached the reverse occurs. Among stars of the 14th and 15th magnitudes cluster-type Cepheids are predominant. This shows us that in a given volume of space short-period Cepheids far out-number those of the classical type. Since they are relatively faint, cluster-type Cepheids must be relatively close to us to be within reach of our instruments, while the brighter long-periods can be observed at greater distances. Now, if in spite of this fact short-period Cepheids are the more numerous, they must really occur much more frequently in space.

The Physics of Cepheid Variation

Up to this point we have considered Cepheids only from the point of view of their light curves, periods, and luminosities. It is time now to turn our interest to some of their physical characteristics.

If we compare the visual and photographic light curves for Delta Cephei, we note that the observed range in variation for the visual curve will be considerably less than that for the photographic curve: $0^m.75$ against $1^m.2$. This difference in range for Delta Cephei is due to a change in color during the light variation. At minimum the star appears redder than at maximum, and since ordinary photographic plates are practically insensitive to red light, the drop in brightness from maximum to minimum light appears larger on the photographs. All Cepheids show the same effect; the photographic range, as a rule, is one and a half times as large as the visual range.

A change in color corresponds to a change in temperature, and it is not difficult to compute from the observed data that the surface temperatures of Cepheids are about 1000 degrees lower at minimum than at maximum. This is no small amount, when compared with their average surface temperatures, which range from 4500 to 8000 degrees. The average surface temperatures are not distributed at random between these limits. There is a definite dependence of temperatures upon period, and the general rule is that the stars with the longest periods are the coolest. Since temperatures are directly connected with spectral classes, we can express this relation by saying that the spectral class of a Cepheid is dependent on the length of its period: the longer the period the later is the spectral class.

Short-period Cepheids have A-type spectra at maximum brightness and F-type spectra at minimum; for intermediate periods—say four or five days—the spectra vary between F and G, while for those of very long period, thirty or more days, the spectral limits are between G and K. This period-spectrum relation is especially important in view of the fact that a similar relation is found among the long-period variables of the Mira Ceti class, which will be treated in the next chapter. In Figure 33, the plot is extended so as to include also the Mira Ceti stars.

The spectra of Cepheids, like those of the great majority of stars, consists of a bright continuous background crossed by numerous dark lines which have been recognized as due to the presence of hydrogen, iron, calcium, etc., in the atmospheres. If we determine the exact wave-lengths of

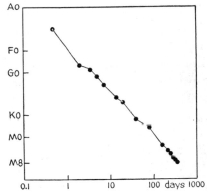

Fig. 33.—The period-spectrum relation for Cepheids and long-period variables.

these lines and compare them with the wave lengths of the same lines as measured in the laboratory, we see that they usually do not exactly coincide, but differ by a fraction of a wave-length unit. This phenomenon is common to all stars and it is well known that it implies motion of the star, or at least of its radiating surface, in the line of sight. According to Doppler's principle, we must observe a shift of the lines toward the red end of the spectrum when the light source is receding from us, and a shift toward the violet when it is approaching. What is more interesting is that in Cepheids

the line-shift does not remain constant, but varies rhythmi-
cally in the same period as that of the light variations of the
star. There is only one possible explanation of the observed
phenomenon, which seems very logical in view of the light
variations; namely that the surface of the star alternately
expands and contracts and that this mechanism produces
the fluctuations in brightness.

To be sure, other hypotheses had been proposed in the
past such as that the line-shifts were due to a second star
revolving around the Cepheid in a period equal to that of
the light variation. But it was soon shown that such a
hypothetical companion would be required by the observations to move inside the Cepheid itself in order to complete
its revolution in the short time of the light variation.

That a pulsation of the star as a whole was possible and
reasonable was suggested first in 1879 by Ritter. He supported his views with a sound physical and mathematical
treatment of the problem—a treatment that contains many
basic points of the modern theory. But Ritter's work seems
to have had little effect and it was not until in 1914 Shapley
exposed the absurdities of the double-star hypothesis, that
most astronomers were ready to consider the pulsation idea.
Finally, in 1919, Eddington published his famous papers
which gave the pulsation theory the sanction of a thorough
analysis.

Eddington imagined that the star would pulsate as a
whole under two opposing actions: gravity, which would
tend to contract the star, and the pressure of the gases com-
posing the star, which would tend to expand it. As the star
contracts, the gas pressure must increase, which should
cause a rise in temperature with yet a further increase in gas
pressure. Driven by inertia, the star contracts beyond its
normal condition of equilibrium, which is the size that it
would have had if it did not pulsate, until a minimum size

is reached and then, because of the steadily increasing gas pressure working as an opposing force it starts to expand. During the expansion the reverse process would take place: the pressure diminishes and with it the temperature, and this continues until the pressure, together with the inertia of the gases, could no longer continue to hold the upper hand over the force of gravity. At that point the star should reach its largest size and must start collapsing again and a new cycle would thus get under way.

In this model of a pulsating star the greatest brightness would be reached when the star attains its smallest size. At first this looks like a paradox, but if one remembers that the brilliance of the star's surface varies as the fourth power of the temperature, it can be visualized easily how this increased brilliance can, when the star is smallest, over-compensate the loss of radiating surface.

The pulsation theory gives us a clear picture of the variations in temperature and is quite consistent with the observed ranges in brightness and velocities in the line of sight. But its most remarkable achievement was the prediction of a period-density relation for Cepheids. Eddington's theory requires that the product of the period and the square root of the density, that is the mass or weight of the star divided by its volume, be nearly a constant for all pulsating stars. This is precisely what is observed; Eddington, C. Payne-Gaposchkin, and Siedentopf have shown that this product has similar values for all Cepheids. Mrs. Payne-Gaposchkin finds that the rule extends also to the long-period variables of the Mira Ceti class, which probably are part of the great family of pulsating stars.

In spite of the successes, Eddington's theory failed to account entirely for some observed regularities. We should expect the star to reach its greatest size at minimum brightness and its smallest size at maximum. Therefore, at minimum and at maximum the surface of the star should be just in balance, neither expanding nor contracting. What we observe, instead, is the greatest velocity of expansion at maximum and the greatest velocity of contraction at minimum. If we plot the observed velocities in the line of sight

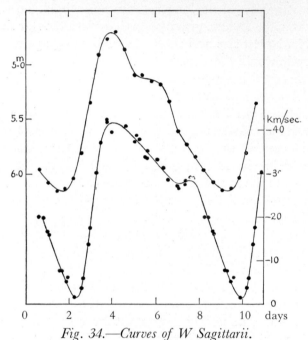

Fig. 34.—Curves of W Sagittarii.

Photographic light curve by Voûte (upper) and radial velocity curve by Jacobsen (lower).

for a Cepheid and compare the graph with the light curve, we have two curves that look very much alike, see Figure 34.

A successful attempt to explain the above discrepancy was made in 1937 by M. Schwarzschild. He imagines that the outer layers of the star can not follow the pulsations of the core with the same rhythm. This will lead to waves running outwards from the interior very much in the way that the successive expansions and contractions of a submerged rubber balloon will cause waves in a pool of water. At the moment when one of these waves reaches the star's surface, we should expect to observe the greatest brightness of the star because we shall then have the greatest pressure in the star's atmosphere. On the other hand we should also observe then, the greatest velocity of approach of the stellar surface which is just what we were looking for.

Thumbs down, then, on Eddington's theory? No! That would be too much. Eddington's theory still works perfectly well for the star's interior; we may even say it works for the greater part of the star, which also, according to Schwarschild, pulsates as a whole. Only in the outer layers does Schwarzschild suggest a sensible departure due to the formation of running waves.

THE DISTRIBUTION OF THE CEPHEIDS

Before we abandon the Cepheids, let us look at their distribution in space. Classical Cepheids are found almost exclusively in the Milky Way or in a narrow band on both sides of it, and this tendency to stay near the Milky Way is most pronounced for the stars with the longest periods. One of the properties of our galactic system is that it rotates around a distant center. The Sun, which is one of the two hundred billion stars of our galaxy takes 200 million years to complete a circuit at the speed of 150 miles per second. The classical Cepheids run perfectly on schedule in this enormous merry-go-round, only, as is customary for such massive stars, they follow a circle around the center even more closely than the Sun.

Cluster-type Cepheids, on the other hand, show in their distribution their more capricious character. They are found practically everywhere in the sky, with only a mild concentration toward the Milky Way. As for their motions, they shoot in all possible directions, sometimes going at terrific speeds and continually breaking the traffic regulations or regularities of the galaxy. It is interesting to note that the globular clusters, the stellar systems in which such variables abound, behave similarly. They show only a slight concentration toward the Milky Way and have high random velocities. Evidently there must be more than a casual association between globular clusters and cluster-type variables.

It almost seems as if the proper place for short-period Cepheids is in globular clusters. Take, for example, the famous globular cluster called Omega Centauri. Of its 154 well-studied variables, all but 13 are short-period Cepheids of groups I and II in Figure 26. (The 13 exceptions are thus subdivided; two classical Cepheids; one long-period variable, probably a foreground star; seven semi-regular; and three irregular variables.) The interesting feature is that in this globular cluster groups I and II do not overlap in period, nor do any of group II exceed 1.35 days in period-length: with the exception of only one star, all Cepheids of group I have periods shorter than 0.48 days and all Cepheids of group II have longer periods. In another globular cluster, Messier 3, we also find the same sharp separation between groups I and II; but instead of occurring at 0.48 days, the division falls at 0.43 days. It looks as if the two groupings were separated at slightly different periods in different clusters. If on the other hand we consider the general run of the short-period Cepheids (that do not belong to globular clusters), we find a considerable overlapping of the two groups, as if the stars had been picked out from different clusters and then mixed together.

The different behavior of short-period and long-period Cepheids is perhaps not so surprising when we consider their respective dimensions. A typical short-period Cepheid, for example RR Lyrae, has a diameter of seven times that of the Sun, while a classical Cepheid with long-period, such as l Carinae, exceeds the sun in diameter by not less than 200 times. That makes l Carinae 25,000 times bigger in volume than RR Lyrae. Long-period Cepheids are, intrinsically, very bright objects. If l Carinae were placed at the same distance as Sirius, it would appear of magnitude -6, about five times brighter than Venus at maximum brilliancy and 60 times brighter than Sirius itself.

THE BETA CANIS MAJORIS STARS

The vast family of Cepheids includes many close and distant relatives. A group of stars which is directly related to the Cepheids, so that its members could well be called their stepbrothers, or even regular brothers, is that of the "Beta Canis Majoris Stars." Only very few, about a score, of these stars are known to date, but that does not mean that they are necessarily very rare. What makes their discovery difficult are their extremely small ranges in brightness, which never exceed a quarter of a magnitude and in most cases amount to only a few hundredths of a magnitude; some stars of the group show no variation whatever. Those stars, although of apparently constant light, are none the less variable stars because of a variation of a more secret nature.

The chief characteristic of the Beta Canis Majoris stars is not their light variations, but the variation of the apparent velocity in the line of sight, revealed by a periodic shift of the lines in the spectra. Close double stars also show such variations of radial velocity, but with these peculiar Cepheids we are certain that our stars are not double because (1) they show only one spectrum, and (2) the variations in velocity are not perfectly regular, as in orbital motion. Astronomers believe that the cause of the phenomenon is a pulsation, as in regular Cepheids, because the Beta

Canis Majoris stars, which show variable light, have the greatest velocity of approach at maximum brightness and the radial velocity curve again runs parallel to the light curve. Beta Canis Majoris stars have all very short periods, from two and a half to eight hours, except that Epsilon Ursae Majoris has a period of almost a day. Since almost the only ways of detecting the variability are spectroscopic, or with the aid of the photo-electric cell, it is difficult to discover the fainter members of this class. Among the brighter members we find such good acquaintances as Beta Cephei, Beta and Epsilson Ursae Majoris, Gamma Bootis, and Delta Aquilae.

Beta Canis Majoris stars are mostly bluish-white stars of spectral class *B*, and it is interesting to note that their spectra are just what they should be according to the period-spectrum relation for Cepheids. It has been suggested that they may actually be a group of regular Cepheids, an addition to the five-group chain, coming before group I in the series illustrated in Figure 26.

THE W VIRGINIS STARS

The Cepheid family has a few prodigal sons. The most conspicuous among them, W Virginis, is, if we judge by the name alone, perhaps even more like a prodigal daughter. This star, whose period is 17 days, has the period, amplitude, spectral class, and steadiness of light curve proper to Cepheids. Its light curve, however, (Figure 35), does not fit in the sequence of Figure 26 and moreover the star has two peculiarities. First, bright hydrogen lines appear in its spectrum on the rise to maximum, and second, its position is 57 degrees distant from the Milky Way, a strange place for a Cepheid with such a long period.

In the globular cluster Omega Centauri we find another star, with a period of 15 days, whose light curve is almost identical with that of W Virginis. Three more stars, in different parts of the sky, all with similar periods have recently been found to show analogous characteristics. The meaning of this group of strayed quasi-Cepheids remains, for the present, a mystery.

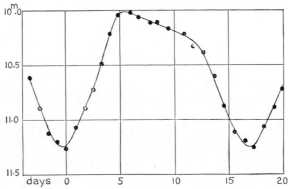

Fig. 35.—Photographic light curve of W Virginis.
(*S. Gaposchkin.*)

The RV Tauri Stars

More loosely related to Cepheids are the so-called RV Tauri stars. They are usually classed together with the semi-regular variables and there are many good reasons for doing so. On the other hand, these stars also show many Cepheid characteristics, so that the confused classifier remains in doubt as to where to place them. We mention them here, because we think that the reader, with the notions about Cepheids still fresh in his mind, will better recognize the links that join them to the Cepheids.

For some mysterious reason, the name RV Tauri seems to have had a special appeal for many persons interested in variable star astronomy and it was almost a fashion, about ten years ago, to call any semi-regular variable with some-

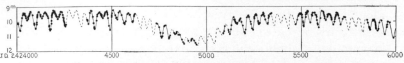

Fig. 36.—Light curve of RV Tauri 1924–1930.

what indefinite characteristics an "RV Tauri Star." Variable star catalogues adopted the classification of these indefinite stars, relying mainly upon the authority of preliminary investigators, and the result was that all kinds of heterogeneus objects, many quite unlike typical RV Tauri stars, were classed as such. It was almost as if so-called RV Tauri stars were those which did not vary as does RV Tauri itself!

RV Tauri is very typical of the group as we limit it today. The light curve is illustrated in Figure 36; we see that it consists of a semi-regular fluctuation with a 79 day period during which there are two maxima of almost equal height and two minima of unequal depth. This double fluctuation, averaging just about one magnitude in each cycle, is superimposed upon a slower wave of 1300 days with a variable amplitude. The amplitude of the 79 day oscillation grows smaller when the 1300-day wave reaches its minimum, and the disparity between the two minima is then greatly reduced. The spectrum of RV Tauri belongs to class *K* and varies considerably from maximum to minimum, thus conforming to Cepheid practice.

The light curves of the other RV Tauri stars do not necessarily possess all the characteristics exhibited by their prototype. In some of them the longer wave may not be periodic, or it may even be completely absent, and in others the difference between primary and secondary minimum may be very small or non-existant. Their chief common characteristic lies in their Cepheid-like spectra. An important point to stress is that RV Tauri stars conform to the period-spectrum relation for Cepheids, when we take as their periods the interval between two successive maxima or minima, irrespective of their height or depth. As a matter of fact, the double periodicity is not of a very rigorous nature even in such stars as R Sagittae and V Vulpeculae (see Figure 37), which exhibit it very markedly. This is shown by the fre-

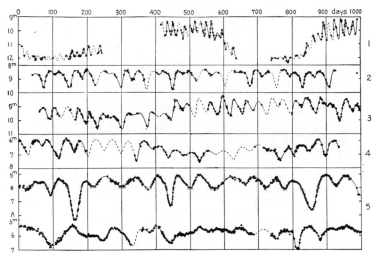

Fig. 37.—Light curves of semi-regular variables related to Cepheid class.

1. SX Centauri; 2. V Vulpeculae; 3. R Sagittae; 4. U Monocerotis; 5. R Scuti (two sections).

quent interchanges that occur between primary and secondary minima. For a few stars, as U Monocerotis (Figure 37), these interchanges occur every three or four cycles, but in other stars, as DF Cygni, they are very infrequent, if present at all.

Defined as above, only 25 stars appear today to belong to the RV Tauri group. In spite of the differences in their light curves, they seem to form a fairly homogeneous group. The intrinsic luminosities appear to be very high, as they should be according to the period-luminosity curve for Cepheids. For the few stars for which an accurate spectroscopic study has been made, the radial velocity is found to be variable, following very nearly the pattern for Cepheids, perhaps with a somewhat greater lag of velocity behind the light variations.

A good friend of many variable star observers, R Scuti, belongs to the RV Tauri group. Its period, 146 days from one primary minimum to the next, is the longest of all and, since the tendency of the RV Tauri variables is to show more and more irregularity for those of longer period, we have for this star a good example of a very fanciful light curve (Figure 37). The star is quite red and its spectrum, although it reaches the K-type at maximum, plunges at minimum into the M-class, which is the realm of the red long-period and semi-regular variables. A few RV Tauri stars show, as they brighten up, the bright hydrogen lines that are a characteristic feature of the red variables. RV Tauri stars occupy, in fact, an intermediate position between the Cepheids and the red variables, tending to bridge the interval between them. Now we have crossed that bridge and stand before the gate that opens into a vast new domain in the realm of variable stars. Let us enter and see, in the next chapter, what is the way of life in that new realm.

5

THE RED VARIABLES

RED STARS HAVE A FASCINATION OF THEIR OWN. IF WE examine the brightest naked-eye stars we shall see that they run through a sequence of various colors; some, like Vega, are bluish-white, others, like Capella, have a yellowish tinge, and still others, such as Antares, present a decidedly reddish hue. Some of the fainter stars are so red that they have been described as "blood-red."

All red stars are not physically alike, and they can be divided into two distinct groups; the red dwarfs and the red giants. The first are decidedly smaller in size than our own sun and of much higher density. The giants are enormous, not only in brilliance, but also in size, with highly attenuated atmospheres, and small, probably dense, cores. Whereas red dwarfs show great stability, and are practically of constant magnitude, the giants are almost always found to be subject to variation in light, as well as in other respects.

The red variables belong to the late spectral classes (see Addenda); a few are of "late" K-type, many of class M, and some of S, R, and N-types. An important feature of these stars, especially of the M-type, is the appearance in their spectra at certain phases of their light changes, of characteristically bright emission lines, due to the radiation of hydrogen. Whenever we find these bright emission lines in the spectrum of a red star, we can be practically certain that we have at hand a variable star with long period. If, on the other hand, these emission lines are absent, or very weak, in a red giant star, we shall find that such a star will either be non-variable, or that it will show very small fluctuations in light of semi-periodic or erratic nature. Thus the *M*-type stars can also be divided into two distinct classes; those with strong and those with weak, or no hydrogen emission lines, which are classed as semi-regular or irregular red variables.

THE LONG PERIOD VARIABLES

We have already mentioned in the first chapter that Mira Ceti was the first star to be definitely established as periodically variable. Its brightness oscillates, generally, between the third and the ninth magnitudes within a period of eleven months. Today we are cognizant of the existance of more than 1300 stars which present the same pattern of variation as does Mira Ceti. Such stars are variously referred to as "Mira" or "Mira Ceti" stars, but more generally they are known as "Long-Period" variables. The term "long-period" refers to the fact that such stars require months to go through their complete cycle of variation, but we must warn you that not all long-period variables are exact counterparts of Mira Ceti.

Most long-period variables have periods between 200 and 400 days, with the greatest number occurring around the 275-day period. There are, however, quite a few variables with periods that fall outside these limits; they range from W Puppis with a period of 120 days to RU Lyncis with a period of 728 days. Only one other long-period star, Har-

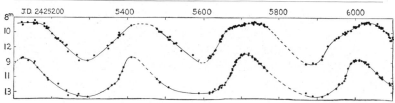

Fig. 38.—Two long-period variables with the same period, but very different light curves.

T Geminorum (upper); S Geminorum (lower).

vard Variable 10446, discovered by Mrs. Mayall in 1940, lies well outside these limits, with a record-breaking period of 1380 days.

Long-period variables present a wide variety of light curves. We have already noted the same for the Cepheids, for which there appeared to be a definite correlation between the length of the period and the form of the curve. At first glance, there appears to be no definite relation between period and light curve for the long-period variables as a whole. Let us take, for example, a group of stars with periods around 300 days. V Ophiuchi, (Figure 45), period 299 days, presents a curve with broad maxima and sharp minima. Contrast this light curve with that of T Hydrae (Figure 39, third curve) which has a period of nearly the same length (290 days), but which has sharper maxima, and a halt, or retardation, on the increasing branch of the curve. Again let us look at the curve of S Geminorum, period 292 days, which has a steep rise following a flat minimum; and at T Geminorum, period 289 days, which shows a flat broad maximum (Figure 38). Truly, here we appear to have a veritable hodge-podge in light curves for approximately the same length of period.

The apparent confusion is clarified to some extent if we separate the variables according to spectral class.

V Ophiuchi, an extremely red star, is of spectral class N, with strong carbon-compound bands. T Hydrae and S Geminorum have M-type spectra, whose principal characteristic is the titanium oxide bands, while for T Geminorum we find bands which are due to zirconium oxide, which designates it as of spectral class S.

Ninety per cent of the long-period variables belong to spectral class M, perhaps more suitably called Me because of the presence of the bright emission lines. The remaining ten per cent is about equally divided between the Se, Ne, and Re spectra. Let us take a look at each class in turn, starting with stars with Me spectra.

Characteristics and Light Curves of Me-stars

Mira Ceti stars—those with Me spectra—usually have very large amplitudes of variation when observed visually, varying from a minimum amplitude of four magnitudes, for Z Scorpii, to a maximum of nearly ten magnitudes for Chi Cygni. A group of about two dozen Me-stars which have smaller amplitudes, as well as some other peculiarities, will be considered later.

The light curves of Me-stars present widely different forms as we pass from one star to another. They may extend from curves with wide maxima and narrow minima, through those with maxima and minima of similar shape, to those with sharply defined narrow maxima and broad flat minima.

While the same variable will, on the average, repeat itself with a fair degree of exactness as regards the general shape of its light curves, there are small divergences from normal between different cycles, mainly dependent on the brightness attained at different maxima, as well as at minima.

A further instability is found in the times of arrival at maximum and minimum light, and in the appearance, on occasion, of secondary waves, or "humps" on the ascending branch of the curve. These humps, which are a prominent feature in the light curves of some stars do not always appear at the same part of the light curve, and may even be absent during a particular cycle of variation (see the light curve of T Geminorum in Figure 38). The descending branch of the light curve is usually free of secondary inflections.

For long-period variables with periods shorter than 200 days we find the greatest change in form of light curve from cycle to cycle. Individual maxima and minima may differ appreciably although the average light curve may not show any pronounced anomalies. The ascending and descending branches of the curves are approximately equal, and the shapes of the minima are not radically different from the maxima. The average range in brightness is five magnitudes (see light curve of X Camelopardalis, Figure 39).

For those variables with periods greater than 200 days there appear to be two distinct groups. For one of these groups we find a number of variables with humps on the light curve which become increasingly more pronounced in those variables for the longer periods. Maximum and minimum maintain approximately the same relative width, and the amplitude is also about five magnitudes.

The variables in the second group at the start of the series —at the 200-day period—differ only slightly from those found in the first group, but as the periods become longer the differences become more pronounced. The minimum becomes increasingly flatter, the increase to maximum becomes steeper and the maximum becomes decidedly narrower. At the same time the range in light variation increases with increasing period, attaining some seven or eight magnitudes for those variables which have exceptionally long periods. Frequently a still-stand develops at the beginning of the rise to maximum. The variables in this group are far more numerous than those found in the first group. The differences between the two series is graphically illustrated in Figures 39 and 40. It is possible that the first of these two groups for stars with periods greater than 200-days is the natural extension from the variables with periods less than 200 days.

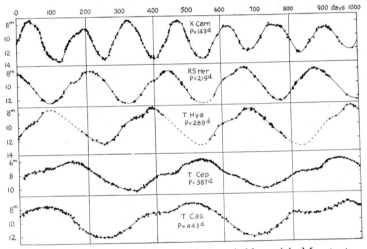

Fig. 39.—First group of long-period variables with Me spectra.

As the period increases, the wave on the ascending branch grows more pronounced, but the amplitude does not change.

One of the outstanding features of the Cepheids, especially the classical Cepheids, is the regularity with which the light variations repeat themselves, not only in length of cycle, but also in the range of the variation; which, of course, means that the light curves are practically identical over years. Such can not be said to hold rigorously for the long-period variables, and perhaps we should not expect the Mira stars to behave as well as the Cepheids.

Although, in a general way, a long-period variable follows an average form of light curve from cycle to cycle, yet
there are distinct variations. The deviations occur mainly at
times of maximum brightness. As a rule the sharper the
maximum the greater the divergence in magnitude at the
maximum stage. Such a marked difference in magnitude
at maximum light is particularly noticeable in V Delphini

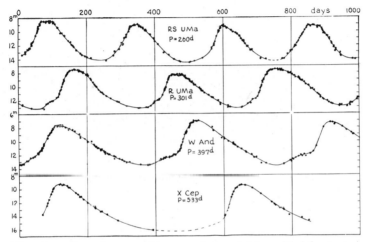

Fig. 40.—Second group of long-period variables with Me spectra.

As the period increases, the ascending branch grows steeper, the
maxima narrower and the amplitude larger.

(Figure 41), when at times the brightness exceeds the ninth
magnitude, while at other times it barely attains the twelfth
magnitude. When the minimum is sharper than the maximum in a given curve, it is the minimum brightness that is
subject to the greatest variations from cycle to cycle.

The magnitude at maximum brightness of Mira Ceti itself
has varied between the second and fifth, while the minimum
magnitudes have ranged between eight and ten. For this
particular star we know that there is a companion, which

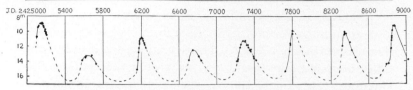

Fig. 41.—Light curve of V Delphini from 1927 to 1938.

is, in all probability, also variable, and which may account in part at least, for the differences at minimum brightness. Chi Cygni has also been known to attain magnitude 3.6 at some maxima, while at other maxima only 6.8. These variations in height follow no apparent rule, but seem to occur purely at random.

PERIODS OF *Me*-STARS

Not only are variations in brightness at maximum very noticeable, but we find that the length of the cycles between maxima or minima, are also subject to considerable variations. One could hardly expect such unsteadily changing stars to have perfectly constant periods. Apart from accidental accelerations and retardations in the times of maxima and minima, due to changes in the shape of the light curve, almost all long-period variables show small irregular fluctuations in the length of individual cycles, oscillating more or less at random around a median value.

Chance, as everyone knows, plays all sorts of queer tricks. If you throw dice, on one night they will show a preference for high numbers, on another night twelves simply will not show up. Something of a similar nature may happen in the random variations of the cycles in our variables. For a few years long cycles will prevail over short cycles, and the variable will seem to have increased its period, but then, a few years later, the order will be reversed and the period will appear to have increased.

Some idea of uniformity, or non-uniformity, of arrival at maximum may be obtained by examination of the diagram shown in Figure 42, which represents, for particular stars, the intervals in time between observed consecutive maxima, here called cycles. For some stars, particularly those of the shorter periods and with sinuous light curves, these cycle

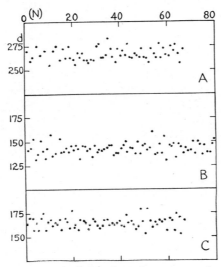

Fig. 42.—*Length of individual cycles—intervals between consecutive maxima.*

A, R Trianguli, period 266 days; B, X Camelopardalis, period 143 days; C, T Herculis, period 165 days.

intervals run very close to the mean period. For others, the deviations from a uniform period are large and somewhat erratic in nature. Although, as a whole, Mira Ceti stars do not show definite and systematic changes in period, at least over the interval covered by the observations, a few have undergone marked alteration; that is their periods have either lengthened or shortened. The most conspicuous case is that of R Hydrae (cycle intervals shown in Figure 43) which,

over a space of 280 years, appears to have decreased the
length of its period of variation from 500 to 400 days, or by
an amount corresponding to 25 per cent of the present
period. R Aquilae is another case in point; it has shortened
its period from 350 days to about 300 days in 80 years. We
can have little doubt of the reality of a change in period for
these two stars. Whether or not the periods will again
lengthen, time alone can tell. S Herculis has shown an
apparent change, between 315 and 300 days, in a sort of
sinuous fashion about a mean period of 307 days.

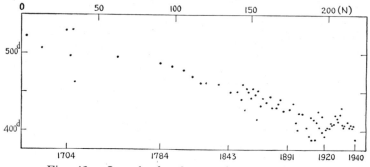

Fig. 43.—Length of cycles, maxima, of R Hydrae.

Showing gradual decrease of period.

PHYSICAL CHARACTERISTICS OF *Me*-STARS

What are the physical characteristics of the *Me*-stars?
How do the stars themselves change as the brightness varies?
In the study of the Cepheids we noted that the surface temperature of those stars decreases as we proceed from shorter
to longer periods. The same rule appears to apply to the
long-period *Me*-stars. This relation becomes still more
significant when we extend the plotting of the temperature-
period relation for the Cepheids to include the long-period
variables; they form a continuous sequence. This was clearly
shown in Fig. 33, Chapter 4, where instead of temperatures,

spectral classes express the same phenomenon. We thus obtain a spectral sequence extending from cluster-type variables—with periods of a few hours—to the long-period stars—with periods of 500 days and more. This period-spectrum relation, which establishes a definite connection between two of the most important classes of physical variables, is of real importance. It seems to indicate that the underlying cause of the light variation is probably the same for both types of variables. This relation is of such significance that C. P. and S. Gaposchkin in their treatise on *Variable Stars* have included under the "Great Sequence" both Cepheids and long-period variables.

Cepheids, as we have already learned, are hotter at maximum than at minimum brightness. The long period variables show the same behavior, and the range in temperature is found to be of the order of 600 degrees. This range is surprisingly small if we consider that the total variation in visual light is, on the average, about six magnitudes, corresponding to a range in intensity of 250 to 1. On the other hand, Cepheids, with a range approximating only one magnitude, have variations in temperature of about 1,000 degrees. The situation appears to be incongruous and merits further study.

Instead of observing the long-period variable in normal visual light, suppose we photograph the star on a plate which is sensitized for infra-red rays. The magnitude of the variable on such a plate will appear to be several magnitudes brighter than when simultaneously observed in a telescope. On infra-red plates Mira Ceti would appear, at times, as bright as the planet Jupiter, and R Leonis, with a visual maximum magnitude of five, would rival Sirius in brightness.

The discrepancy between magnitudes as observed in infra-red and normal visual light is not surprising when we

consider that long-period variables are red. What does prove to be a surprise is that, as observed on infra-red plates, the total range in variation is very small, not over a magnitude and a half.

If we proceed to measure the light variations with a radiometer, which records the total amount of radiation received from a star, we find a still smaller amplitude of variation for Mira variables. For Chi Cygni, with a visual range of nearly ten magnitudes, Pettit and Nicholson obtained a radiometric amplitude of only a magnitude; for most long-period variables, the range barely reached a full magnitude. Thus we note that the total radiation does not vary over a much larger range than for Cepheids.

How can we explain such a discrepancy between the real range of radiated energy and the range in variation of light as seen by the eye? As everyone is well aware, the eye is sensitive only to a narrow region of the spectrum, that which extends from wave-lengths on the edge of the "violet" rays, to those on the edge of the "red" rays. Long-period variables emit, for the most part, long-wave infra-red radiation which our eye can not discern, so that actually we see only about five per cent of the total amount of radiation sent out from a star such as Mira Ceti when at maximum.

As the star cools off on its way to minimum, the main portion of its radiation is shifted still farther into the infra-red, leaving only a dwindling fraction of light within the limits of sensitivity of the eye. Therefore our eyes will observe much larger fluctuations than an instrument which is capable of measuring the star's radiation over a greater range of wavelength. This explanation, however, does not account for all the differences found between the radiometric and the visual range. Joy of Mount Wilson computed the visual range of variation of Mira Ceti from the radiometric curve and found that it should be of the order of

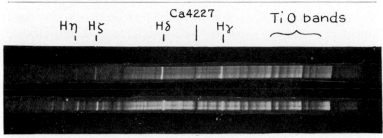

Fig. 44.—Spectra of Mira Ceti.

(Upper) Nov. 11, 1926, near maximum; (lower) Oct. 9, 1940, three months after maximum. (*Photographed at the Harvard Observatory.*)

3.5 magnitudes, whereas we know that the visual range is about six magnitudes. Thus there is still an outstanding difference to be accounted for. Where does the remaining two magnitudes difference come from? It is probably associated with the so-called "bands."

If we examine the spectrum of Mira Ceti (see Figure 44) we note that it is crossed by heavy absorption bands, due mainly to titanium oxide, especially in the visual region, and that they grow increasingly stronger as the star cools and fades in passing from maximum to minimum light. In other words, more and more visual light is cut off by these bands as the star becomes fainter. Thus band absorption can account for a full magnitude of the visual range and only relatively small differences still remain unexplained.

A possible further explanation is offered by Merrill who suggests that the atmospheres of long-period variables become less transparent to visual radiation as the temperature diminishes. The low atmospheric temperature of these stars, below the boiling point of many common substances, would permit the formation of a cloud layer, the thickness of which would increase as the surface of the star grows cooler. This veil of clouds would consist of small liquid and solid particles, somewhat analogous to our terrestrial clouds, and could account for strong dimming effects with only small changes in temperature.

It is not unreasonable to suppose that the veil is composed mainly of titanium oxide in the M-type stars, like Mira Ceti, of zirconium oxide in the S-type stars, and of carbon-compounds in the N-type stars. The different reactions to temperature of these differently compounded veils, could explain, in part, the difference in the shape of the light curves of stars of different spectral types. This veiling effect would not appreciably affect the total radiation for the stars themselves, because, as we well know, infra-red rays can more easily pass through clouds.

Accordingly, we know that, in spite of the excessive fluctuations in visual light, long-period variables fall pretty well in line with the Cepheids; the main trouble was with our eyes!

Let us again return to the problem of the bright hydrogen lines which we mentioned earlier in the chapter, and which are exceedingly important. There is a whole row of these bright lines, designated as Hα, Hβ, Hγ, Hδ, etc., which start at the red end of the spectrum and proceed in the order given toward the violet end. On normal blue plates Hγ and Hδ are the strongest, because Hα and Hβ lie beyond or near the limit of sensitivity of the plate, and Hϵ usually plays hide and seek behind a strong absorption line. The remaining lines from Hζ on, located in the ultra-violet portion of the spectrum, are weak.

When a Mira variable is at its brightest phase the Hγ and Hδ lines are very conspicuous—so bright in fact that they serve at a glance to reveal the presence of the long-period variable among the hundreds of other simultaneously recorded stellar spectra. At minimum brightness, however, practically no bright lines are to be seen in the spectrum. They make their first appearance about midway between minimum and maximum, while the star is increasing in brightness, reach their greatest strength somewhat after maximum light is attained and die out shortly before minimum. While the hydrogen lines do vary in intensity with light changes, they are not exactly in phase with the light, lagging behind by almost a sixth of the period of the star's variation.

The bright hydrogen lines have proven no small problem for the astronomer to unravel. It was natural to believe that, because hydrogen is the lightest of all known gases, the origin of the lines would be in the uppermost strata of the star's atmosphere, but how could the hydrogen atoms acquire sufficient energy to become excited to the stage necessary in these higher layers? We now have evidence that these lines originate in the lower layers, but where they get their energy is still not clearly understood.

The bright hydrogen lines are not the only bright lines found in the spectra of long-period variables. There are a few other bright lines due to the light metals, but the majority of the visible lines are dark and even the bright lines have along side of them, dark absorption lines. The behavior of the two sets of lines is decidedly at variance, and regrettably our picture of parallel behavior between Cepheids and long-period variables is spoiled, whether we consider bright lines or dark lines. In Cepheids we found that the absorption lines reveal a maximum speed of expansion near maximum brightness, and the most rapid rate of contraction at minimum light. For the Mira stars, just the reverse is true for the absorption lines. The bright emission lines on the other hand, show greatest velocity of approach, that is of expansion, when they reach their greatest intensity. The phenomenon presents a puzzling condition, and to understand better the problem we must consider first the physical nature of these stars.

Long-period variables are enormous stars, even larger than Cepheid variables, although their total output of energy is somewhat less because of their lower temperatures. Reliable measures of the volume of Mira Ceti place this quantity at 30 million times that of the Sun, or more than 40 million million times that of the Earth. If Mira Ceti were placed in the center of the solar system, where our sun is located, its outer surface would extend as far as the orbit of Mars, so that the Earth would move entirely inside the star. The total mass of Mira Ceti probably does not exceed twenty times that of the Sun, and it may not exceed it by as much as ten times. This leads us to the extremely low average density of one third of a millionth of the Sun's density. The pressure in the lower layers of the star's atmosphere must be of the order of one millionth that of normal atmospheric sea-level pressure on the Earth, comparable to the pressure attainable with the average vacuum pump. Theory shows that in spite of the extremely low density of the outer layers, the core of the star may be very dense.

The "visual" absolute luminosity of long-period variables at maximum brightness is not far from magnitude zero. But here again, since our eye receives only a small fraction of the total output of energy of the star, the total radiation would indicate an absolute luminosity of about minus four (-4). This may seem high for a star, yet it is not as high as that found for some Cepheids with longer periods. In the period-luminosity relation for classical Cepheids we found a regular increase of brightness with increasing period, therefore we must conclude that this relation can not be extended to long-period variables.

There is still another marked difference between Mira stars and Cepheids. The latter are found to stay gradually closer to the Milky Way as we proceed from the shorter periods to the longer periods. The classical Cepheids with longest periods revolve at a fixed speed about the center of our galaxy in almost circular orbits. The long-period variables, however, appear to be revolving around the center of the galaxy at all possible speeds, more as do the cluster-type Cepheids. Although long-period variables are found in and near the Milky Way, they are also found in other regions of the sky, even as far away from the plane of the galaxy as the galactic poles.

With this information at hand, we may now draw a few conclusions. It seems evident that long-period variables are, like Cepheids, pulsating stars, but because of their different physical structure, the pulsation must manifest itself differently in the outer layers of their atmospheres. Recently R. M. Scott attempted to apply to Mira Ceti itself the theory of Cepheid pulsation as worked out for these stars by M. Schwarzschild, and apparently with considerable success. Scott turned his attention to the emission lines rather than to the absorption lines and tackled the problem on the hypothesis that the bright hydrogen lines are formed in a layer very close to the radiating surface of the star. Thus, by studying the radial velocity of the bright lines, we should obtain a fair picture of how the surface of the star pulsates.

Scott's assumption leads to very reasonable conclusions as to the physical properties of the gaseous matter within the star. His success was somewhat of a surprise to those astronomers who had believed that it would be the observed velocities of the dark absorption lines that would reveal the law of pulsation in the star's surface, as had been found for the Cepheids. In Mira Ceti stars the absorption lines probably originate in the higher levels of the extensive atmosphere, and when these levels are reached by the waves which start from the center of the star, their pulsations follow the pulsations of the surface with some delay.

As for Cepheids, so also for long-period variables, only the denser part of the star would pulsate as a whole, according to Eddington's star model. But for long-period variables the denser portion is a much smaller fraction of the whole star than is the case for Cepheids, and therefore it is expected that the mechanism of Schwarzschild's running waves rules a larger part of the star's body. (See Chapter 4.)

Other Types of Long-period Variables

So far we have been concerned mainly with the *Me*, or Mira Ceti, stars chiefly because this group comprises ninety per cent of the total, and also because we seem to know a good deal about them. The *N*, *S*, and *R*-type stars, though relatively few in number, must not be overlooked. The long-period *N*-stars, which also show emission lines in their spectra, and therefore are known also as *Ne*-type stars, present some of the same features as the *Me*-type stars. On the whole, *N* stars have smaller amplitudes of variation, nearer to four magnitudes, than to six or eight. On the average, their periods are longer than those of most Mira stars, extending from 254 days for Y Persei to 579 days for S Aurigae, with a preponderance around 420 days. The spectra of *N*-type stars are mainly confined to red and infra-red light, making them the reddest stars in the sky. They present strong spectral bands which have been identified as due, in part, to carbon, cyanogen, and hydro-carbons. There are only about two dozen *N*-type long-period variables known.

The light curves of *N*-stars show, in general, very broad maxima and narrow minima, as indicated in Figure 45, with the ascending branch seldom steeper than the descending branch. In many cases, especially for the stars with longer periods, the decline to minimum is steeper than the rise to maximum. Humps on the ascent and near maximum are the rule rather than the exception, in some instances resembling a secondary maximum and minimum.

We know of two *R*-type variables, S Camelopardalis and RU Virginis. The former has a period of 326 days, with a

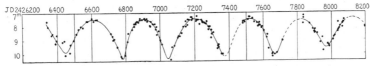

Fig. 45.—Light curve of V Ophiuchi (Spectrum Ne).

Ne variables are characterized by broad maxima and narrow minima.

range in light variation of 2.5 magnitudes; the latter has a period of 436 days, and a range of 4.5 magnitudes. Like the *N*-type stars, those of *R*-type have very broad flat maxima and sharp narrow minima. A light curve of S Camelopardalis is shown in Figure 46. The *N* and *R*-type stars appear to be closely allied.

The *Se*-type variables do not differ radically in their general behavior from *Me*-stars; in fact they may be con-

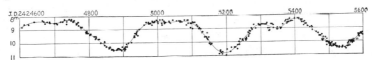

Fig. 46.—Light curve of S Camelopardalis.

Spectrum Re.

sidered as closely related to the *M*-type variables as are the *N*-type stars to the *R*-type stars. The main difference to be found between *Se*-stars and *Me*-stars is that the former reveal the preponderance of absorption bands due to zirconium oxide in place of the titanium oxide bands found in *Me*-stars. In a few *Se*-stars both zirconium and titanium oxide bands are found equally abundant. As we have hinted before, the different reaction of the zirconium bands to temperature changes may be the main cause of the differences found in the light curves. Zirconium oxide can exist at higher temperatures than can titanium oxide.

The light curve of R Camelopardalis, a typical *Se*-star, (see Figure 47) illustrates the great width and flatness at maximum, a feature seldom found in *Me*-stars. Where we found that *Me*-stars show humps in the curve at the beginning or end of the rise to maximum, the *Se*-stars show a

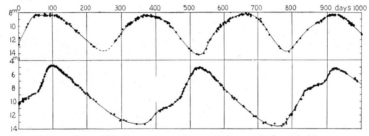

Fig. 47.—Light curves of two long-period variables.

R Camelopardalis (upper, spectrum Se) and Chi Cygni (lower spectrum Me and Se). Se variables are characterized by broad maxima, or large humps at a place midway on the rise to maximum.

tendency for the humps to appear at a place midway on the rise to maximum. The visual amplitudes of the *Se*-stars are, on the average, equal or greater than those of *Me*-stars, and they show a distinct tendency to increase with increasing period. *Se*-stars number only about two dozen, with periods ranging from 200 to 600 days, and their physical characteristics, radial velocities, dimensions, etc., are not markedly different from those of the *Me*-stars.

Peculiar Long-period Variables

Not all long-period variables, even those of the *Me*-type, are without their peculiarities. A remarkable abnormality is found in R Centauri, and four others of similar kind. The light curve presents a regular alternation of deep and shallow, or faint and bright minima, while the maxima are almost of equal brightness. The light curve of R Centauri is shown in Figure 48. The star has the spectrum of a normal long-period variable of 280 days yet the assigned period, assumed as the interval in time between two successive faint

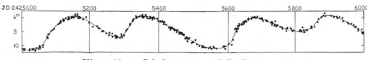

Fig. 48.—*Light curve of R Centauri.*

minima is 558 days. The question then naturally arises; is the period of the star to be assumed as the interval in days between two successive maxima, or minima, regardless of depth, thereby agreeing with the period-spectrum relation, or is it the time between two successive deep, or shallow, minima? A similar predicament was found for the RV Tauri stars in relation to normal Cepheids, and perhaps we should

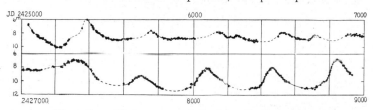

Fig. 49.—*Light curve of R Aquarii 1927–1938.*

infer that R Centauri stars bear a special relation to ordinary long-period *Me*-stars, as RV Tauri-stars are related to Cepheids.

There is another long-period star which is perhaps unique among variables; the star R Aquarii. For many years it appeared to follow the general behavior pattern laid down for *Me*-stars, with a normal amplitude of variation of some

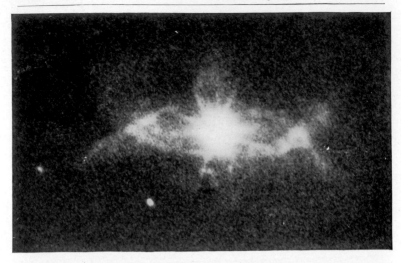

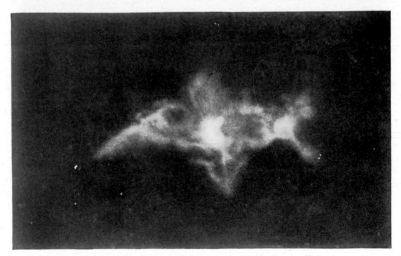

Fig. 50.—Nebulosity around R Aquarii.
Photograph (upper) and drawing from the same photograph (lower).
(*Photographed with the 100-inch Mount Wilson telescope.*)

four or five magnitudes, in a period just under 400 days. In the year 1928 there set in a series of variations of decidedly smaller and smaller amplitude until, in 1932, there was very little change in magnitude, the star remaining at about its magnitude of nine. The assigned period appeared to persist, however, and in 1934 the star began to vary again in a more normal manner, at first with the resumption of its usual fainter minimum magnitude, and later attaining its customary bright maximum. In 1937, and from there on, the star has behaved as was its habit in earlier years. The light variations during the critical years are shown in Figure 49.

The spectrum of R Aquarii is one of the most complicated for a long-period variable. Its main portion is a late *M*-spectrum, with bright hydrogen lines, quite normal for a star with such a long period. But superimposed upon the *Me*-spectrum is another which has the appearance of being produced by a hot blue star. This latter spectrum is very faint, even absent, when the light variations of R Aquarii are normal but it increases in intensity during the epochs of perturbed fluctuations in light. Besides these two types of superimposed spectra, Merrill has found evidence of some bright "nebular" lines, evidently associated with a faint irregular nebulosity in which the star is embedded (see Figure 50).

It is not easy to obtain a clear picture of just what is going on in such a complicated star system as is presented by R Aquarii. The riddle yet remains to be solved!

The Red Semi-regular and Irregular Variables

You have all heard of how strong a man was Samson while he kept his locks unshorn, but what a weakling he became when his locks were cut off by Delilah. The bright hydrogen lines seen in the spectra of red stars may be likened to Samson's locks. Whenever we see these lines shine forth in all their splendor, we are certain that we have a variable star with a large variation in light, five or more magnitudes, within a definite period of time; in other words we have a regular long-period variable. When, on the other hand, these emission lines appear only faintly for a short time, or fail to show up at all, then we know that the star, if variable to any extent, is a weakling whose feeble oscillations are performed with an unsteady rhythm; a star with semi-regular or irregular variations.

For many years no distinction was made between long-period and semi-regular variables. When a red variable with small amplitude was found it was simply classified as a long-period variable, if it showed some evidence of periodicity; otherwise it was placed among the irregular variables. Today we know that there is much less difference between an "irregular" and "semi-regular" red variable than between a semi-regular and a long-period variable.

One of the distinctive features of semi-regular variables is the small visual amplitude of variation, often less than one magnitude and seldom reaching two magnitudes or more. The main difference between them does not lie in the smaller range in variation but in the degree of regularity of variation. The light curve of AF Cygni (see Figure 51), shows at once that the curve is by no means a replica on a smaller scale of the light curve of a Mira Ceti star. For stars of the Mira Ceti-type the length of a single cycle may deviate from the mean period, or cycle, by five or ten per cent, but in AF Cygni the deviations may reach or exceed a hundred per cent with a continuously changing amplitude and shape of light curve. Although there is little doubt of the reality of the fundamental period of 88 days for AF Cygni, it can be seen that an attempt to derive a mean light curve for the star over several years would be out of the question. One can see from Figure 51 that, on occasion, the

length of the cycle doubles and remains doubled for a long
time.

Another feature often present in the group of semi-regular
variables is a slow semi-periodic fluctuation of the median
brightness, with such an effect that the light curve seems
actually to be the result of two waves of different lengths
(see V Ursae Minoris, Figure 51). These slow fluctuations
usually extend over many cycles and in a few cases, as in UZ

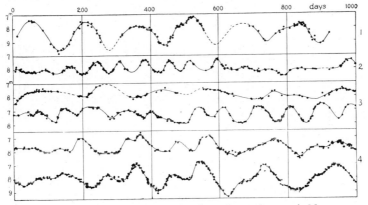

Fig. 51.—Light curves of red semi-regular variables.

1. X Monocerotis; 2, V Ursae Minoris; 3, AF Cygni; 4, Z Ursae
Majoris.

Persei, TW Pegasi, etc., they have larger amplitudes than
has the fundamental variation itself. Such a condition was
found to exist for the RV Tauri stars, which class has many
characteristics in common with the semi-regular variables.
That this slow fluctuation is a phenomenon similar to that
observed in RV Tauri stars is shown by the fact that at
minimum phase the amplitude of the fundamental variation
considerably diminishes, and for a few stars actually vanishes
to almost zero for a few cycles.

The degree of regularity, perhaps better termed irregularity, varies greatly from star to star. At one end of the

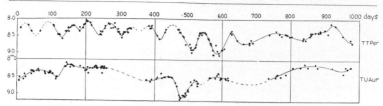

Fig. 52.—Light curves of two irregular variables.

TT Persei (upper) and TU Aurigae (lower). TT Persei can still be considered as a semiregular variable in spite of the many irregularities, while TU Aurigae is definitely irregular.

sequence we find such stars as X Monocerotis (see Figure 51) which, although not so regular as a normal Mira Ceti star, maintains a fairly steady rhythm in its variations. The sequence then progresses through such stars as V Ursae Minoris, AF Cygni, (Figure 51) and TT Persei (Figure 52) until at the other end we find stars whose cycles of variation are so variable that they show no evidence of periodicity. Such stars, as shown in the light curve of TU Aurigae, Figure 52, can be definitely classed as "Irregular." It is worthy of note that some of these semi-regular variables with larger amplitudes, such as X Monocerotis, show at some phases faint hydrogen emission lines in their spectra.

It is not easy to imagine a truly irregular phenomenon in Nature, and it is possible that these "Irregular" stars appear to be so mainly because we have not been able to analyze the complicated processes which concur to make them vary as they do. As with some meteorological phenomena on the Earth, we know that the lack of regularity is due to the excessive number of factors which conspire to produce a seeming confusion.

The periods of semi-regular red variables range from 42 days, for TX Tauri, to 530 days for UW Aurigae, with the greatest concentration around 180 days. S Persei, of spectral

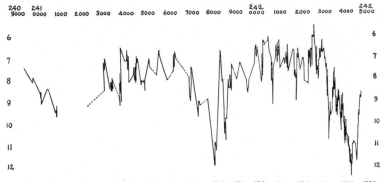

| 240 9000 | 241 0000 | 1000 | 2000 | 3000 | 4000 | 5000 | 6000 | 7000 | 8000 | 9000 | 242 0000 | 1000 | 2000 | 3000 | 4000 | 242 5000 |

Fig. 53.—Light curve of V Hydrae 1883–1926.

class $M5$, has a still longer period, but it is an exceptional star in more ways than one. It has a dominant period of around 835 days, with a probability that other periods are involved. H. H. Turner thought that periods of 840, 1120, and 3360 days prevail; and T. E. Sterne recently derived two distinct periods, one 810 days, the other 916 days, which combined in such a manner as to produce the resultant light curve, at least for a number of years.

Another semi-regular star of special interest is V Hydrae, of spectral class $N5$, one of the reddest stars of this type. Here we appear to have a star which varies through a moderate amplitude in a period of about 530 days, with strong evidence of a secondary period of 18 years super-imposed on the 530 day period, and a maximal amplitude of more than six magnitudes (see Figure 53).

In several semi-regular stars the variation is complicated by the intrusion of a second wave which sometimes, as for U and RY Camelopardalis, may have a completely independent period of its own, and in other cases simply defies any appearance of regularity, as for example in Z Ursae Majoris, which has a period of 197 days, upon which is imposed an apparently irregular variation (see Figure 51). It is probable that there are many stars now classed as irregular, which would, under more detailed analysis, reveal themselves as subject to complicated multiple periodicities.

We find among the semi-regular and irregular variables, many of the old friends of the naked-eye star gazers. Brightest of all is Betelgeuse, or α Orionis, which shows semi-regular waves of 140 to 300 days which appear to be superposed upon a still slower fluctuation with a cycle of six years; and yet the observed range of light variation hardly exceeds a magnitude, from 0.2 to 1.2. Alpha Herculis also varies in a semi-regular fashion, and α Scorpii, known as Antares, has been suspected of being a variable of this same type. Other well known red stars which show semi-regular variations are η Geminorum and μ Cephei, Herschel's "garnet" star.

It is not by pure chance that so many of the red M-type variables are visible to the naked-eye. We know the distances of a few of them; they are among the intrinsically brightest, as well as the largest stars in existence. Betelgeuse has an absolute magnitude of -4, μ Cephei -3. Measures of the angular diameter of Betelgeuse, the first star to have its diameter measured directly with the Michelson 20-foot interferometer attached to the 100-inch reflector by Pease in 1920, showed a value of $0''.04$, which, at the star's known distance, corresponds to about 350 diameters of the Sun. Subsequent measures indicated that the diameter of Betelgeuse varies along with its light, between 200 and 400 solar diameters; the reality of the pulsation hypothesis was thus confirmed. Measures of α Herculis and α Scorpii reveal even greater diameters, of the order of 400 and more times that of the Sun. This all goes to show that the red semi-regular variables are perhaps comparable in size to the Mira Ceti variables, or even larger, and that their absolute brightness is somewhat greater than that of Mira Ceti itself at maximum brightness.

The spectra of the semi-regular and irregular variables are more or less similar to those of the Mira Ceti stars; mainly of Class *M*, with some *N*-types mixed in and a few *S*, *R* and *K*-types. One feature to be noted is that there appears to be no correlation between the length of the period and the spectral class, or temperature, as was found for Cepheids and Mira Ceti stars. Hydrogen emission lines appear only weakly in some of the semi-regular stars, with a behavior quite unlike that in Mira Ceti stars, as the lines remain visible only during the increase in light from minimum to maximum. A similar behavior is observed in a few anomalous stars with Cepheid-like periods (W Virginis and RU Camelopardalis) which show bright hydrogen lines, and also in the RV Tauri star R Scuti. That this spectrum peculiarity indicates a link with Cepheids is pointed out also by the existence of three semi-regular variables with periods of about 100 days, whose spectra at maximum are very similar to those of Cepheids with longer periods (Class *G*0) while at minimum the spectra resemble those of normal *M*-type stars. The light curve of one of these three stars (SX Herculis) at times looks very much like those of long-period Cepheids. There would seem to be a more continuous bridge between Cepheids and semi-regular variables than between Cepheids and Mira Ceti stars.

About 250 red stars with small range in variation are known today. Of these, 116 are classed as semi-regular, 40 as irregular, and for the remainder the available data are too scanty for classification. We might be led to assume from these figures that such red variables are not very numerous in comparison with the Cepheids and Mira Ceti stars. There may be many more red variables of this type, however, which have escaped detection because of the difficulty of measuring their very small variations in light. Photo-electric observations by Stebbins and Huffer have indicated that practically all red giant stars show slight variations, generally of three to four tenths of a magnitude or less.

If we could include all red giants in the group of irregular and semi-regular variables, and they would naturally belong in this class if they were variable to even a small extent, this group might easily rank as the richest of all the classes of variables.

6

EXPLOSIVE STARS

*T*HE SUDDEN APPEARANCE OF A BRILLIANT, NEW OBJECT IN
the heavens was regarded by the ancient Chinese as an
omen, not only one which presaged pestilences and calami-
ties, but also one which might give promise of victories in
battle, and of abundant crops. Doubtless the new objects
seen in the early centuries were not all bright comets, but in
some cases at least, bright novae, or new stars, were among
the celestial visitors which made their appearance between
the years 2679 B.C. and 1230 A.D. The identification of
these objects—whether comets or new stars—appears not to
have concerned the Chinese annalists as much as the recording of the events which followed their sudden appearances.

In Europe and the Near East, the people were apparently
less impressed by changes in the sky. The only new star
recorded during the 4000-year interval from the beginning of
the Egyptian civilization to the Middle Ages was the brilliant star of the year 134 B.C. which was also observed by the
Chinese and which, according to Plinius, led Hipparchus to
construct his famous star catalogue. Since that time no new
stars appear to have been seen, except for two or three
dubious records, until 1572, when the spectacular star in

Cassiopeia, visible even in broad daylight, raised superstitious fears among the populace. This new star has been called "Tycho's Star," because the Danish astronomer, Tycho Brahe, was one of the first to see it, and to study its light variations.

It is remarkable that only 32 years later another extremely bright star made its appearance, this time in the constellation of Ophiuchus, and that another of the greatest astronomers of all time, Kepler, was there to witness its variations. The star in October 1604 shone with a brightness equal to that of Jupiter, and was visible as a naked eye object until March 1606.

From that time on, astronomical records are more complete and it is probable that in the northern hemisphere at least, no new star of the first magnitude escaped the attention of star-gazers. The improvements in the construction of telescopes and the completion of star maps led to the discovery of a few of the fainter new stars—or "Novae," as they were called—but it was not until 1901 that another first magnitude nova made its appearance. As this particular new star was typical of most novae that have been observed since then, we shall describe its activities in considerable detail.

NOVA PERSEI 1901

The nova was first detected by T. D. Anderson on February 21, 1901. Dr. Anderson, a Scottish clergyman, was walking home late that night when, looking at the constellation of Perseus, he noticed a strange star of the third magnitude in the region between the famous variable star, Algol, and the brightest star of the constellation, Alpha Persei. He did not need a star map to recognize that the star was an intruder, since a person only slightly acquainted with constellations knows that there is no bright star between

Algol and Alpha Persei. He communicated his discovery to the Greenwich Observatory, which immediately spread the news to the whole world.

At the Harvard Observatory, where the now famous collection of celestial photographs had already been started some years before under the direction of E. C. Pickering, it was found that the new star was actually not completely new. A number of early photographs revealed that in the position of the nova there had previously existed a faint star of about the thirteenth magnitude which showed small fluctuations in light. It so happened that the Perseus region had been photographed at Harvard only two days before Dr. Anderson's discovery, and the plate showed the star still at normal minimum brightness. Thus, in less than two days, it had brightened from the thirteenth to the third magnitude, an increase of 10,000 times in luminosity—a veritable explosion!

Between February 21 and 23, the star continued to increase in brightness, but at a somewhat slower rate, until it reached a maximum at magnitude zero, about the brilliance of Capella and Vega. The total change in brightness was accordingly about thirteen magnitudes, and had been accomplished in less than four days. Directly after the nova reached zero magnitude, it began to decrease with a fair degree of rapidity, although slowly in comparison with its rise. Six days after maximum, the nova had faded to the second magnitude, and two weeks later it had reached the fourth. At this stage a series of oscillations set in, with a periodicity of about four days, and an amplitude of a magnitude and a half. These fluctuations lasted for several months, during which time the star continued to fade, until it was no longer visible to the naked eye. The rate of diminution in brightness decreased steadily, and the nova finally returned to its former state, at magnitude thirteen, eleven years after it had started on its spectacular adventures. At present it displays the same irregular fluctuations, with an amplitude of two magnitudes, that it showed before its outburst.

Most novae, as far as we can judge, display a rapid rise and an enormous change in brightness during their earliest stages of activity. This behavior suggests an explosive phenomenon as the cause of the outburst. Until a few years ago, it was believed, because of the lack of evidence to the contrary, that each nova performed once, and once only. Astronomers attributed nova outbursts to heavenly catastrophes, such as the encounter, or near encounter, of two stars, or of a star and a large comet, or to the breakdown of the internal equilibrium of the star with consequent collapse and explosion. Any one of these picturesque events could probably not happen in the same star more than once. Today we know, however, of novae that have exploded two, and even three times, and also of variable stars that erupt as do the novae, but on a smaller scale, every few days or months. Novae have definitely descended to the rank of variable stars.

TYPES OF NOVAE

Although the nova of 1901 in Perseus was a very typical one, we must not conclude that all novae behave, even approximately, alike. A glance at Figures 54 and 55, which illustrate an arrangement of the light curves of 18 novae, shows that there are large differences to be found among them. Actually, only one known star, Nova Aquilae 1918, (see Figure 56) presented in the course of its activity the same general sequence of activity as Nova Persei, 1901. Incidentally, the nova in Aquila, which reached the magnitude −1.4, almost the brightness of Sirius, was the brightest nova since Kepler's of 1604. Other novae, as for example,

CP Lacertae, the second-magnitude nova of 1936, followed the behavior of Nova Persei, but they did not show the semi-periodic fluctuations on the decline. Nova EL Aquilae, a fainter object that flared up in 1927, exhibited fluctuations, but these were slow and irregular. Nova Cygni 1920 staged a mild increase in light three months after maximum, and Nova XX Tauri of 1926 had a broad primary maximum, with a secondary increase of about one magnitude six months after the original outburst. By the way, some novae as you will have noted, have been given regular variable-star designations, and others not; all novae of recent years have been named, rather than dated and numbered, and the practice is being continued.

In the upper part of Figure 54, you will find the light curves of three peculiar novae, each of which lingered for a few months near maximum, where it showed rapid fluctuations in brightness, then faded some nine or ten magnitudes, only to brighten again to a secondary maximum and, finally, start the regular decline. The most conspicuous of the three was Nova (DQ) Herculis, which almost reached the first magnitude around Christmas 1934. The behavior of DQ Herculis in the first few months continued to follow so closely that of T Aurigae of 1891, that one could almost predict what the former would do next—for example when the very sudden drop in light would occur. In spite of their slow development, these peculiar novae brightened very rapidly, as is shown by T Aurigae, which was fainter than magnitude 13.2 only two days before it was photographed as a star of the fifth magnitude. Novae of this type have sometimes been referred to as "Slow" novae, in comparison with such "Fast" novae as Nova Persei 1901 and Nova Aquilae 1918, but in view of their quick rise and rapid decline to a secondary minimum, this designation may seem inappropriate. Moreover, Figure 54 indicates that there is a con-

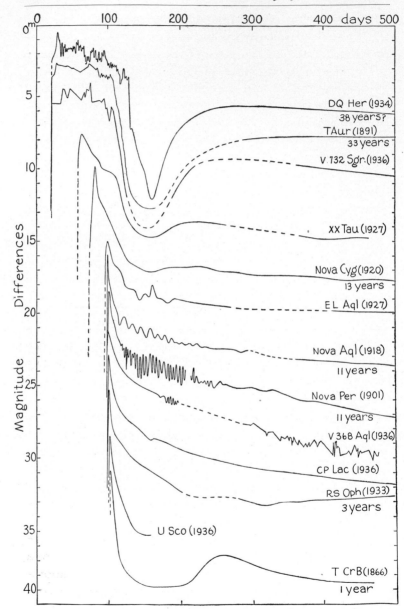

Fig. 54.—For descriptive legend see opposite page.

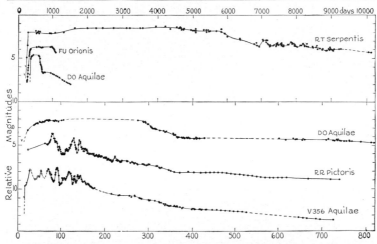

Fig. 55.—Light curves of five slow novae.

In the upper part of the figure the time scale is considerably contracted. The light curve of DO Aquilae is repeated in both upper and lower sections to allow a quick inter-comparison of the two sets of curves.

tinuous series of light curves from Nova Persei 1901 to DQ Herculis 1934, so that it would be very difficult to tell where in the series the "fast" novae end and the "slow" novae begin.

In Figure 54, we have given for each nova the time taken for its complete development, from the outburst to the epoch when it came back to normal minimum brightness. As we see, this time increases from a dozen years for stars of the Nova Persei type to over 30 years for those of the Nova Herculis type. The few novae at the bottom of the figure will be the objects of our future attention and may be left momentarily aside. It must be remarked that the magnitude reached by the nova when it settles down again after the

Fig. 54.—Light curves of 13 Fast Novae.

Under the name of the Nova is given, whenever known, the time required for the star to again reach normal minimum brightness.

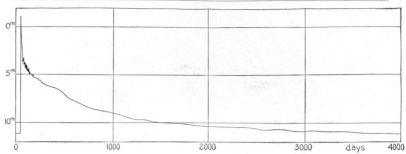

Fig. 56.—Light curve of Nova Aquilae 1918 from outburst to 1929.

outburst is practically the same as before the explosion, at least within the limits allowed by the errors of observation. This fact is very important because it shows that the nova as a whole is not very much disturbed by the explosion, which therefore must be a rather superficial phenomenon.

Some genuinely slow novae are shown in Figure 55, especially the three in the upper part of the diagram. RT Serpentis, for example, took more than a month to rise from magnitude 14.0 to 11.0, and FU Orionis required seventy days to increase four magnitudes. Also in other respects, the changes in brightness of slow novae, differ considerably from those of the novae that we have met so far. DO Aquilae remained practically constant at maximum for more than 200 days, but this length of time is still short compared with the 600 days for FU Orionis and the 15 years for RT Serpentis! This latter star certainly establishes the record for slowness among novae; today, 32 years after its explosion, it has reached in its evolution the same stage that Nova Aquilae, 1918, reached a week after its outburst.

OCCURRENCE AND LUMINOSITY OF NOVAE

Seventy-two novae have been discovered in our galactic system since the beginning of the twentieth century. The present average rate of discovery is thus nearly two novae a year. This, however, is far from being the actual number of novae that appears annually in our galaxy. Most of them escape our attention, especially when they are very faint, or near the Sun.

Paradoxical as it may seem, we can get a better picture of the number of novae in a stellar system by studying not our own galaxy but one of the near-by external systems. There all the stars are crowded into a small area of the sky and any strange object is easily detected, if it is bright enough. The best studied galaxy is the Andromeda Nebula, also known as Messier 31 (see Figure 57). Not less than 116 novae had been discovered in that system prior to 1934, and the discoveries

Fig. 57.—The Andromeda Nebula.
(*Photographed by Ritchey at Yerkes Observatory, with 24-inch reflector.*)

were made at an average rate of about ten a year. The
nebula is, however, not photographed day by day, and one
must expect that even here a considerable number of novae
has been missed. Hubble estimates that the average rate of
appearance of novae in the Andromeda Nebula is around
thirty a year. Novae have also been found in a dozen other
extra-galactic systems, including the Magellanic Clouds.

A surprising fact emerges from the study of novae in the
Andromeda Nebula: the brightness which they reach at
maximum is found to lie within rather narrow limits of
magnitude. The average maximum magnitude of a nova in
this nebula is 16.4 and most of them do not differ more than
half a magnitude from that value. The extremes of magnitudes at maximum are 15.0 and 17.7. This small dispersion
shows that the phenomenon of novae, in spite of the variety
of light curves, is subject to certain regularities.

Since the distance of the Andromeda Nebula is known
from a study of Cepheids and other stars, we can easily
compute the intrinsic, or "absolute" luminosity of an average nova at maximum. The brightness turns out to be
$-5^m.8$ and is in good agreement with the absolute magnitude -5.6 derived for the novae in the Magellanic Clouds.
In other words, novae at maximum are just about as bright
as the brightest non-varying stars which we know; actually
they are a little fainter than a few of the very brightest,
which exceed magnitude -7.

The time spent by a nova at maximum brightness is only a
very transitory stage in its evolution and from it alone we
learn nothing regarding the condition of the star before the
explosion. It has been suggested that any star may explode
at some time and become a nova. Some popular writers
have tried to picture what would happen to our planet
and its inhabitants if the Sun were to burst suddenly into a
nova. Some have gone so far as to see in the phenomenon of

sun-spots a sign of the instability of the Sun—an omen of imminent danger. It is easy to show that such suppositions are groundless.

If any given star could become a nova, then, since normal stars have a large diversity in absolute magnitude, the amplitude of each nova should be different in order that the brightness reached at maximum should be the same. Nothing of this sort is observed. Whenever it has been possible to accurately measure the total range in brightness of a normal nova, it has proved to be practically always the same—about 13 magnitudes. This shows that novae start from the same general level of brightness, about 13 magnitudes fainter than minus six (-6), the value reached at maximum. Thus all novae, before their outbursts, are presumably stars with absolute visual magnitudes between $+6$ and $+8$.

A further restriction that apparently a star must satisfy, if it is to become a nova, is indicated by an inspection of the colors, or spectra, of novae before explosion. Only in a very few cases has it been possible to get such information, because of the extreme faintness of practically all novae at normal minimum brightness; but in every observed case the star was found to be white, or bluish-white, before the outburst. Thus we reach the very important conclusion that novae are probably recruited from white stars of absolute magnitude near plus seven $(+7)$, that is, they are not very different from those mysterious objects that go under the name of "white dwarfs."

Only very few "white dwarfs" were known until recently, but this is no indication that these stars are actually rare in space, because their detection is made difficult by their intrinsic faintness. In recent years many more white dwarfs have been discovered through the persistent efforts of some astronomers, especially Kuiper and Luyten. These dwarf stars are extremely dense, some of them having a mass about twice that of the sun, compressed into a volume no greater than that of our earth; and they have very hot surfaces. The most famous of the white dwarfs is the companion of Sirius, or Sirius B. A pint of the material of this star would weigh about 30 tons. Such high-density conditions, however, are found only among the very small white dwarfs, those of absolute magnitude around $+12$ or $+14$. The stars from which novae originate are certainly somewhat less compact in their structure, though yet very dense when compared with average stars like the Sun. Whether the few white stars with absolute magnitude plus seven $(+7)$ that have been found in recent years are potential novae, is still an open question. The logical conclusion from all this discussion is that all stars that are not white and dwarfish seem to be pretty safe from the danger of explosion. In particular, no such fear need to be entertained for our Sun, which is a normal yellow star.

"Fast" novae, such as Nova Persei 1901 and Nova Aquilae 1918, take about a dozen years to come back to a steady level of brightness. Novae of the "dip-and-recovery" type, such as DQ Herculis, require a much longer time to return to normal, as was shown by T Aurigae which prolonged its explosive career for 33 years. "Slow" novae, of course, persist as novae for a still longer time. At its present rate of decline, RR Pictoris 1925, should reach its normal minimum brightness by about the year 1970. As for RT Serpentis, although very little is known about this star, it can be said with a fair degree of probability, that its complete evolution will require more than a century.

THE PHYSICS OF NOVAE

What are these explosions, anyway? Astronomers have gathered a great mass of observational material concerning the changes in brightness and in spectrum of the novae, and the reader will naturally ask how far have we progressed toward the solution of the problem. We hope that he is not expecting too much, because the interpretation of nova-explosions is still a rather hazy one. A few stages have been investigated with considerable success, but concerning others, we are still much in the dark, especially in regard to the first act of the drama, and the underlying causes. We shall describe briefly the observed facts and then present a possible interpretation.

When a nova approaches its greatest brightness it usually shows a continuous spectrum crossed by narrow absorption lines which, in its general characteristics, is not greatly unlike that of a giant A-star, such as α Cygni (see Figure 58). The greatest intensity of the continuous spectrum lies in the ultra-violet region. The red part of the spectrum seems to be more intense in slow novae than in fast novae. Occasionally there may be some weak emission bands accompanying the absorption lines on their red edges. The intensity of the emission lines decreases generally until at maximum they seem to disappear completely. All absorption lines are displaced toward the violet by amounts which according to the Doppler principle, correspond to velocities of expansion ranging from a few hundred up to 1000 or 2000 kilometers per second, and even more. All this indicates that at this stage the light of the nova originates from a rapidly expanding surface, a sort of giant bubble blown out by internal forces.

Immediately after maximum light has been attained, a decided change takes place in the general aspects of the spectrum. Bright emission lines appear to the red side of the absorption lines and grow more conspicuous for the next few days. The absorption lines become more numerous and more complex. Many absorption lines consist of several

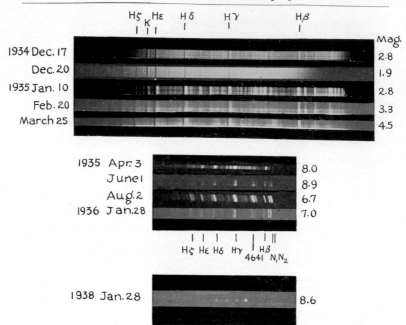

Fig. 58.—Spectra of Nova (DQ) Herculis.

The maximum brightness (1^m4) was reached on the night of December 22–23, 1934.

components, each showing a different velocity. Usually the low-velocity components gradually disappear and new high-velocity lines make their appearance. The velocities of expansion are sometimes exceedingly high, as for example for CP Lacertae which attained a maximum speed of 3790 kilometers per second, or eight and one-half million miles per hour. As one would expect, slow novae show smaller velocities, hardly in excess of 1000 kilometers per second.

With decreasing brightness comes a general weakening of the continuous background of the spectrum, so that the absorption lines become less and less clearly recognizable. The bright emission lines, on the contrary, apparently gain in intensity, in width, and also in number, as new lines of more and more highly ionized elements appear. Among these lines there are the so-called "nebular lines"; sometimes these are already visible at maximum, but their intensity becomes greater as the nova grows fainter.

The nebular lines are so named because they are the principal feature of the spectrum of a gaseous nebula. For a long time many of these lines could not be identified with those of any known terrestrial substance and therefore it was thought that they were produced by an unknown mysterious element which was given the name of "nebulium." In 1927 Bowen, on the basis of atomic theory, showed that they are actually produced by singly and doubly ionized oxygen and nitrogen. The probability that these mutilated atoms radiate—emitting only the nebular lines—is extremely low and therefore, according to Menzel, a small amount of gas, as that available in a laboratory, could not give anything but very weak lines. In nebulae, however, where the quantity of gas is large, the total number of atoms capable of emitting nebular lines is so great that the lines may appear very strong. The failure to detect most of the nebular lines in the laboratory is responsible for their being called "forbidden" lines. Recently, however, they have been produced in the laboratory. The failure of the ordinary lines to appear strongly in the nebulae is due to the low density and to the fact that the atoms in the nebulae are so far away from the source of excitation; a blue hot star.

In novae the "Nebular" lines apparently gain in strength as the continuous background weakens. The spectrum completes its evolution from the absorption type into an almost pure emission spectrum as the brightness of the nova fades to some six magnitudes below maximum. Practically all the light of the star then emanates from a few wide bright lines.

Two years after maximum, with the fading of many of the earlier emission lines, especially those of the Balmer series of hydrogen, and the changing in the relative intensity of the more persistent ionized-oxygen lines, the spectrum of a nova usually becomes almost identical to that of a planetary nebula. After a few more years, the nebular lines grow fainter, until by the time the nova has reached its pre-nova brightness, only a continuous strip of light, with but little evidence of lines, remains. The star is at its normal stage again.

It is important to remark that each successive stage in the evolution of a nova occurs at a point in the light curve where the brightness has dropped by a definite amount below maximum light. In the case of DQ Herculis, see Figure 58, the absorption spectrum remained practically unchanged during the three months or more that the star was hovering near maximum, but between April 1 and 3, 1935, when it suddenly decreased by three magnitudes, the change to an emission spectrum took place almost over night. On the other hand, the recovery in brightness to the seventh magnitude following the sudden deep drop to minimum in the nova did not reverse the development of the spectrum. These strange events must all be kept in mind when we attempt to find an explanation for the nova phenomena.

If we are uncertain about why and how novae explode, that does not necessarily mean that we are unable to connect at least some of the observed facts, or to find the answer to some of the problems raised by the development of the nova spectrum. For example, when we observe that, at a certain phase, the spectrum of a nova looks like that of a planetary nebula, we conclude that at that moment the light of the nova is produced by a process very much like that which causes the planetary nebulae to shine. If we did not know how the light of such a nebula is produced, this statement would have very little significance, but today, thanks to the work of Zanstra, Menzel, and others, our understanding of these strange objects has considerably increased. We now know that planetary nebulae, as for example the famous "Ring Nebula" in Lyra, see Figure 59,

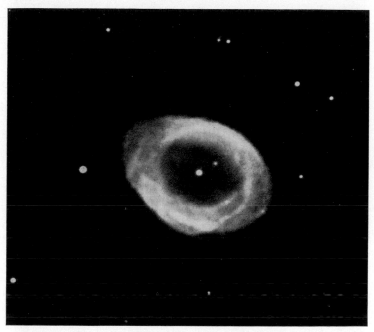

Fig. 59.—The "Ring Nebula" in Lyra.

(*Photographed at the Mount Wilson Observatory with the 60-inch reflector.*)

are composed of a shell of tenuous gases at the center of which is a small, but exceedingly hot star. This star is found to be dwarfish and blue, not unlike the novae before and after their explosions, and emits almost entirely invisible, ultra-violet radiation. Its radiation is so energetic, that it excites the atoms in the nebulous shell and causes them to re-emit light in the visible part of the spectrum. This phenomenon of re-emission of radiation in the longer wave-lengths is not dissimilar to what occurs when a fluorescent substance is energized by ultra-violet radiation.

Therefore, when novae show a nebular spectrum we can safely say that their light must come from a tenuous shell surrounding the star itself; furthermore, as the bright nebular lines show velocities of expansion, we can infer that the shell itself is then expanding. The reality of the expand-ing shell is confirmed by direct observations of novae. In 1916 Barnard discovered a faint nebulosity surrounding Nova Persei 1901 that expanded at the rate of $0''.4$ a year. Its shape, as revealed later by actual photographs, was quite irregular and there was a fan-like extension which in 1919 reached to a distance of $20''$ from the star. Similarly, Nova Aquilae 1918 showed in October 1918 a planetary disk, $0''.65$ in diameter, which grew at the rate of $2''$ a year. It had moved out by $16''$ in 1926, giving the star the appear-ance of a real planetary nebula. Nebulosity was also observed around Nova Cygni 1920, Nova Ophiuchi 1919, and RR Pictoris 1925.

RR Pictoris presented still another strange phenomenon. In 1928, three years after its explosion, Van den Bos and Finsen at Johannesburg saw the star surrounded by what appeared to be three satellites of unequal brightness. One of these disappeared in 1930, but the other two were still visible in 1934, and they had then drawn apart from the star, as if they had been ejected by it. Similarly, DQ Herculis was recognized as an expanding double star in July 1935 by Kuiper, and V356 Aquilae was seen double by Finsen two months after maximum. It is certain that those "Satellites" were not stars but just tenuous irregular patches of ejected material.

The expanding nebulosities around novae must not be confused with another phenomenon which has the same

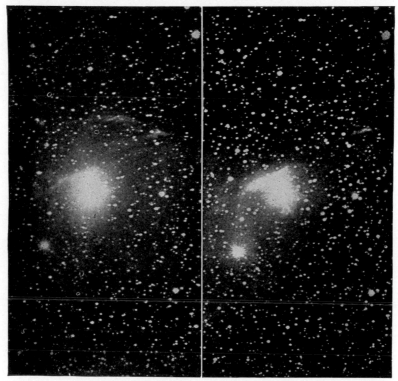

Fig. 60.—Nebulosity around Nova Persei 1901.
(Left) Nov. 7–8, 1901; (right) Jan 31–Feb. 2, 1902.

appearance but which results from a completely different
cause. Shortly after the outburst of Nova Persei 1901,
nebulous patches were detected around the star (see Figure
60) and observations showed that these patches, while
continually changing their shapes, were receding from the
nova at the incredible apparent velocity of twenty minutes
of arc per year (for comparison the diameter of the moon
measures 30 minutes of arc).

From the magnitude reached by Nova Persei at maximum
we can estimate its distance at about 400 light years, and at

such a distance an apparent velocity of 20 minutes of arc a year corresponds to a real speed of about 180,000 miles per second. The reader has probably already recognized the familiar figures for the velocity of light.

What apparently happened was the following: the nova is embedded in a dark irregular nebulosity, similar to many others found in various parts of the sky. When the star exploded, only to fade again a few days later, a short lived, but strong, light pulse was sent out in all directions and travelling at the speed of 186,000 miles per second, brightened up for a few days those nebulous patches farther and farther away from the theater of explosion.

Returning to the real ejection of the nebulosity, we note that one of the most interesting questions concerns the possibility of relation between novae and planetary nebulae. Although some astronomers argue that planetary nebulae are the product of nova-like explosions, it is not yet possible to say whether or not ordinary novae could produce planetary nebulae such as the Ring Nebula in Lyra. As far as our present evidence goes, the nebulosities around most novae grow very thin after some years and finally disappear completely. Explosions of a more violent nature, as those of the super novae which we shall mention soon, could be held responsible for the production of persisting planetary nebulae, but this hypothesis meets with considerable difficulty in the low expansion velocities, less than 100 kilometers per second, observed in some of these nebulae. It is also possible that a planetary nebula is formed little by little by successive explosions of a star, as is suggested by a few strange looking nebulae which show several irregularly interlaced rings. A remarkable fact is that the stars at the center of planetary nebulae seem to have just about the intrinsic luminosities of ordinary novae at normal minimum light.

Very suggestive are some recent observations which point to the possibility that the "Crab Nebula," an irregularly shaped gaseous nebula in Taurus (Figure 61), originated from an actually observed nova. According to Duncan this

Fig. 61.—The Crab Nebula.
(*Photographed at the Lick Observatory.*)

nebula expands at the rate of $0''.134$ per year and N. U. Mayall finds spectroscopically that the velocity of expansion is about 1300 kilometers per second. From these data we can deduce that the nebula should have started about 800 years ago. It happens that in the year 1054 the Chinese recorded a brilliant new star, whose position roughly corresponds to that of the Crab Nebula. In view of the uncertainties of the measures, a difference of 100 years is well within the limits of possibility.

Summarizing observations and theory we find first that the surface of the nova swells, and continues to radiate like any other stellar surface, presenting a continuous spectrum. This swelling produces an enormous increase in the apparent brightness of the star. After a while, however, the expanding surface becomes thin and transparent. Under these conditions it would not contribute appreciably to the total brightness of the nova, but the central star, stripped of its outer layers, sends out such a powerful ultra-violet radiation that the thinning envelope is excited to shine somewhat in the way that neon in an advertising sign is made luminous by electric discharges. This brilliant glow by far out-shines the star itself, which in the meantime rapidly fades, and this phenomenon explains why the continuous spectrum is practically unobservable, although the bright lines are very strong. As the envelope grows thinner and thinner and finally dissipates almost entirely, so also the bright lines fade and long-exposure photographs are needed to record them. Eventually these lines disappear, leaving only the very faint continuous spectrum of the star at normal minimum brightness.

All this seems rather satisfactory, but we have not yet answered the final question: why do nova explode? This matter is still pretty much in the air. It seems, however, that considerable progress has been made by astronomers during the past few years, especially by the rejection of the old "catastrophic" theories. According to Unsöld and Biermann, there is a zone of instability under the surface of very dense stars, such as novae. Normal stars are in "radiative equilibrium" throughout; this means that the outflow of energy from any volume of the star is exactly equal to the energy received from the interior, plus any amount of energy that might be liberated inside the volume itself. If radiative equilibrium did not rule, turbulent currents would be necessary to reestablish a smooth distribution of energy inside the star. In this critical layer inside novae the physical conditions would be such as to allow a state of radiative equilibrium only within extremely narrow limits. The slightest disturbance, whether for internal or external reasons, would perturb the equilibrium and cause a violent commotion in that part of the star which lies outside the critical layer. Biermann even finds, theoretically, a justification for the existence of such a layer in dwarfish white stars.

RECURRENT NOVAE

We have mentioned the possibility that a nova might explode more than once. We have a very interesting example of observed reoccurrence in the case of RS Ophiuchi which appeared for the first time in 1898 and was then listed as a normal nova. In 1933 Loreta of Bologna, Italy, while observing the well known variable Y Ophiuchi, detected

Fig. 62.—Leslie C. Peltier. Prominent American amateur observer.

the presence of a strange star which proved to be the old nova RS Ophiuchi. Fortunately he first saw the star while it was increasing in light. A few days later Peltier of Delphos, Ohio, independently observed the star, as had been his habit for a dozen years or more, and found it bright, but evidently on the decline. While it was not surely known before that RS Ophiuchi was a recurring nova, Peltier appears to have had a "hunch" that it might some day reappear. He kept a steady watch. The hunch proved correct!

When the light curve of RS Ophiuchi in 1898 was super-imposed upon that of 1933, the coincidence was remarkable; apparently in this instance whatever happened on the first occasion was exactly duplicated at the second appearance. Let us again examine Figure 54. At the bottom, we find the light curves of RS Ophiuchi, U Scorpii, and T Coronae Borealis. We can see from the light curve of RS Ophiuchi, the best observed of the three, that it does not differ essen-tially from that of CP Lacertae; as for its spectrum, at maximum brightness it looks very much like that of any other novae and followed a normal development during the decline, save for the appearance of five mysterious bright lines usually present in the spectrum of the solar corona, but hitherto never observed in any other star. There are, how-ever, some more differences between RS Ophiuchi and most normal novae. Fast novae, such as CP Lacertae, require, on the average, a dozen years to return to normal minimum, whereas RS Ophiuchi required in 1933 only three years to return to its normal state. Ordinary novae have a range in brightness very close to thirteen magnitudes, while the total amplitude of RS Ophiuchi was only eight magnitudes. Finally, normal novae have been observed to explode only once, whereas RS Ophiuchi has had already two observed maxima.

U Scorpii is also remarkable, having exploded three times, in 1863, 1906, and 1936. On each occasion the brightness reached the ninth magnitude and the shape of the curve, at least in 1863 and 1936, when the star was well observed, was the same. T Coronae Borealis, a short-lived nova with range of nine magnitudes, was seen to explode only once, but if we may judge by the form of the light curve and the range of amplitude, we may well suspect it of being a recurrent nova. Another nova of this same type is T Pyxidis, normally a fourteenth magnitude star. In 1890, 1902 and 1920, it increased to the sixth or seventh magnitude. On two of these occasions it lingered at maximum for several months, not unlike DQ Herculis.

The rise to maximum in recurrent novae is extraordinarily rapid. U Scorpii in 1936 increased at the rate of three quarters of a magnitude per hour shortly before maximum. RS Ophiuchi was still more rapid; in 1933 there were found two photographic plates taken only two hours and twenty minutes apart just at the time when the star was in the middle of its rise. On the second photograph RS Ophiuchi appears slightly more than two magnitudes brighter than on the first, a rate of increase of about a magnitude per hour.

Super Novae

Let us now abandon the realm of ordinary novae to make the acquaintance of a type of highly explosive star which makes the explosions of normal novae appear like mere sneezes. As we have seen, the average apparent magnitude reached at maximum by the hundred odd novae observed in the Andromeda Nebula is 16.4. In August 1885 a new star appeared almost exactly in the center of this nebula, reached the sixth magnitude, and then faded regularly until in February 1886 it had become fainter than the fifteenth magnitude. If this Nova had flared up in the nebula itself, and there was little doubt about that—in view of its position so close to the center—then it had reached at maximum a brilliancy 10,000 times greater than that of an average nova. The Andromeda Nebula itself, with its billions of stars, appears of the fourth magnitude, that is to say only two magnitudes brighter than this special nova at maximum.

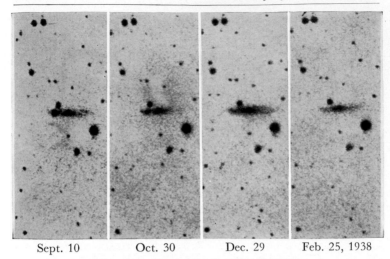

Sept. 10   Oct. 30   Dec. 29   Feb. 25, 1938

Fig. 63.—Supernova in N.G.C. 1003.

The Supernova is near the left edge of the nebula.

There were still some grounds for believing that this nova might be a foreground star which belonged to our own galaxy, and not to the nebula, but these ideas have been definitely dispelled during recent years by further discoveries of similar novae in other galaxies. Most of these discoveries—over 30 supernovae are known to date—were the fruit of a systematic study undertaken at the Mount Wilson and Palomar Observatories by Zwicky, Baade, and others. Zwicky's search involved the continuous photographic examination of hundreds of galaxies in certain regions of the sky, such as in Coma, Virgo, and Ursa Major, where the galaxies are very numerous. Several supernovae have also been discovered at the Harvard Observatory in the course of extensive surveys of external galaxies.

The brightness of these supernovae at maximum nearly equals, on the average, that of the galaxy in which they appear (Figure 63). If the galaxy is a very large one, like the

Andromeda Nebula, then the supernova will usually appear a few magnitudes fainter; but if the galaxy is relatively small, then the supernova may even outshine the whole system by a magnitude or so. For example, a supernova, which in 1937 appeared in a faint, spiral nebula in the constellation of Canes Venatici, reached the eighth magnitude, while the nebula itself did not exceed the thirteenth!

Shapley was the first to recognize, in 1917, that novae actually fall into two classes, normal and super, with a wide divergence in their intrinsic luminosities at maximum brightness. As we have seen, ordinary novae reach on the average, absolute magnitude -6, while the average luminosity of supernovae at maximum is near -15. In view of the fact that our Sun is a star of absolute magnitude $+5$, we may conclude that supernovae, at maximum, are intrinsically twenty magnitudes, or 100,000,000 times, brighter than the Sun.

A supernova that appeared within a distance of 100 light years from our solar system would shine in the sky brighter than the full moon. Such a phenomenon was probably never observed in historic times, in spite of highly poetical statements of Chinese annalists who described some new stars as brilliant even as the Sun itself. We know, however, of two probable supernovae that actually appeared within our galaxy, but at great distances from us; these were the famous stars of 1572 and 1604. The light curves of these two exceptionally bright novae were very similar to each other, but differed considerably from those of normal novae. If, on the other hand, we compare the light curves of these two novae with those of supernovae in an external galaxy (Figure 64), we find that there are many points of resemblance. In general, supernovae show broader maxima, slower and steadier declines after maximum, and, moreover,

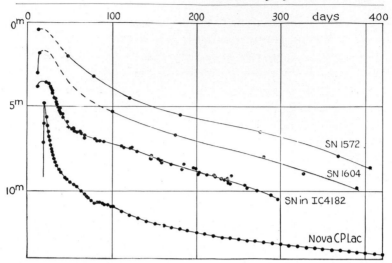

Fig. 64.—Light curves of the bright novae of 1572 and 1604 compared with the light curves of a supernova and an ordinary nova.

they show a slight acceleration in the decline some ten months after the explosion.

The occurrence of two supernovae in a galaxy in the short space of 32 years is very remarkable in view of the general rarity of the phenomenon. This particular situation may be merely accidental, for since 1604 no nova has been detected in our stellar system that is even suspected of having been a supernova.

According to Zwicky, the probability of the occurrence of a supernova appearing in an average galaxy is of the order of one every 600 years. There are, however, other facts to be considered. Supernovae have never been observed in bright galaxies of the elliptical type, but only in spirals, and among spirals they seem to prefer those with very open, clearly resolved arms. Thus we would expect the frequency of super-novae to be greater in the open, spiral galaxies, of which our own galaxy seems to be one. This view is supported by the recent discovery of not less than three supernovae in an interval of sixteen years within the open-type spiral galaxy, NGC 3184, and of two supernovae each in the galaxies NGC 4321 and 6946 at intervals of 13 and 22 years, respectively.

Little was known about the spectrum of a supernova before R. Minkowski of Mount Wilson began his pioneer work on them. In fact he had investigated the matter to the point where he could, from the examination of the spectrum of a recently discovered supernova, predict with surprising accuracy exactly how many days or weeks before that date, the star was at maximum. At first glance the spectra of supernovae appear to be quite unlike those of normal novae. They show an almost continuous background with two regions especially bright, one in the violet and one in the orange, and are crossed by comparatively narrow and strange looking bands. Recent studies by Whipple and Payne-Gaposchkin point to the possibility, however, that the observed continuous background is not actually continuous, and that the appearance of "bands" is only an illusion. They think that the spectrum is, in reality, mainly composed of bright lines, such as are found for normal novae, and that these lines are so broadened by the terrific velocities of expansion involved, that they overlap, giving the illusion of a continuous background. The velocities required to produce line-broadening to such an extent would be of the order of 5000 kilometers a second. The spectra of supernovae undergo, in the course of their evolution, marked changes which are correlated with the light curve.

LESSER EXPLOSIONS

We find in the category of variable stars, a few which behave in some respects not unlike the novae. Picture the difference in degree between violent volcanic eruptions, which occur at relatively long intervals of time, and the lesser and more frequent eruptions of geysers, and you have by analogy the difference between novae and U Geminorum stars. In the U Geminorum stars the explosions, if such they can be called, are comparatively mild, reaching five magnitudes at the most; but they recur at short intervals of a few days, weeks, or months.

Take, for example, U Geminorum which, together with SS Cygni, shares the honor of being the most popular star of this group. Normally U Geminorum is very faint, of the fourteenth magnitude, so that an instrument of fair size is needed to see the star at minimum. You may watch the star for two, three, or four months, or even longer, and notice little if any variation in its brightness. Then on a certain night, when you have abandoned all hope of finding the star at maximum, you turn the telescope for another routine estimate of the star, and there it is!—shining so brightly that you may need to use the finder if you wish to make a reliable observation. The increase in brightness is sudden, for usually it does not take the star much more than twenty-four hours to increase from the fourteenth magnitude to full maximum at the ninth magnitude. If you are fortunate enough to catch the variable at the beginning of the rise, it is a real thrill to watch its brightening hour by hour.

All U Geminorum stars flare up at very irregular intervals, so that it is absolutely impossible to make any forecast of the time when the explosions will take place. For U Geminorum itself (see Figure 65) all possible intervals have been observed between the limits of 62 and 257 days. There is, however, a statistical cycle of variation for each star of this type. If you count the number of observed maxima of U Geminorum in a ten-year interval, say from 1900 to 1910, you will find that it does not differ radically from the number of maxima observed during another ten-year interval, for example from

1930 to 1940. Each U Geminorum star is characterized by what may be called an "average" period, although there is no evidence for real periodicity. We find that the average interval between two successive maxima is 97 days for U Geminorum; 50 days for SS Cygni, and 17 days for SU Ursae Majoris, which is another star of this same type.

The most active of all U Geminorum stars is AB Draconis, with an average cycle of 13 days. The total duration of a maximum, i.e., the interval from the time the star starts to

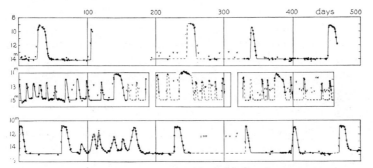

Fig. 65.—Light curves of typical U Geminorum stars.

U Geminorum (upper); SU Ursae Majoris (center); SS Aurigae (lower).

increase in brightness, to the time when it again reaches a constant minimum magnitude, is about six days for this variable, but there are times when it lasts for only three days; a few hours to brighten, a short stay at maximum, and then two days for the descent. The shortest observed interval between two successive maxima for this star is nine days, but the record in shortness, eight days, seems to belong to SU Ursae Majoris, for which the average cycle is, however, 17 days.

Very fast U Geminorum stars seem to form a group of their own. There are nine stars known with average periods between 13 and 26 days; they all have a relatively small

amplitude, from 2.5 to 4.0 magnitudes, and they show
maxima of very unequal length. As a rule, when the star
brightens more than is customary, the maximum is of
longer duration. Some stars, such as AY Lyrae and SU
Ursae Majoris, see Figure 65, sometimes show spectacular
"supermaxima" which last almost as long as a whole average period, during which time the brightness exceeds by a
full magnitude that of all the other maxima. X Leonis, a
star with an average period of twenty-five days, does not
show supermaxima, but instead presents long and short
maxima which sometimes regularly alternate for a year or
more. Interesting are some periods of frantic activity in SU
Ursae Majoris, when maxima follow each other at less
than half the normal interval, and when the range decreases
considerably. One of these peculiar spells is shown at the
beginning of the light curve of this star in Figure 65.

Proceeding to U Geminorum stars with longer cycles, we
first find an interesting group of four stars with periods
between 50 and 78 days; this group includes SS Cygni, SS
Aurigae, RU Pegasi and UU Aquilae. These stars never
have supermaxima, but instead, sometimes show a different
type of maximum, which has been called "anomalous."
These anomalous maxima are characterized by a slower rise
which lasts several days instead of approximately twenty-
four hours. One of them is shown in the light curve of SS
Aurigae in Figure 65, next to the last. Anomalous maxima
are usually symmetrical in shape, the rise lasting just about
as long as the fall.

If one again examines the light curve of SS Aurigae, he
will notice the wild, zig-zagging fluctuations at the left.
These erratic variations occur without warning, after years
of perfect normality. SS Aurigae showed no sign of irregular
behavior during the first twenty years after its discovery, but
in 1929 it began a series of marked eccentricities, starting

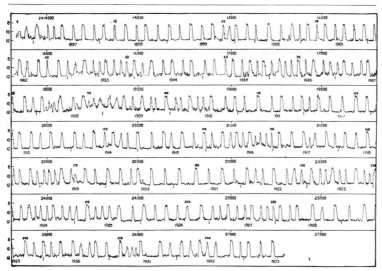

Fig. 66.—Light curve of SS Cygni 1896–1933.

to rebrighten, for example, before it had actually reached normal minimum brightness. The peculiar behavior lasted for several months, after which the star returned to its normal condition.

SS Cygni is even more frequently subjected to such irregular spells (see Figure 66). The most important ones took place in 1907 to 1908, 1930, and 1933 to 1934, but there were milder attacks in 1916 and 1936. RU Pegasi is a curious star which is irregular most of the time and only on rare occasions does it qualify as a regular U Geminorum star. On the other hand the fourth star of the group, UU Aquilae, although yet scantily observed, seems to be rather regular.

Finally, we have five stars with longer average periods, from 97 to 340 days, among which there is U Geminorum itself. These stars are never subjected to irregular spells, nor do they show anomalous maxima. In U Geminorum long and short maxima alternate sometimes for many years, but from time to time the succession is inverted. All five show rather large ranges, around five magnitudes.

The spectra of the U Geminorum stars, following some early researches on SS Cygni by Adams and Joy, have been further extensively studied during the past two years by Elvey and Menzel. The spectra all show the same character-istics. At minimum the spectrum consists of bright, wide, hydrogen and helium lines, with only a faint trace of a continuous background. When the star brightens, the con-tinuous spectrum grows increasingly stronger; at the same time the bright lines do not increase in intensity at the same rate. Shortly before maximum the continuous background becomes so bright that the bright lines are no longer dis-tinguishable, and the spectrum appears as a continuous strip of light, with its greatest strength in the ultra-violet region. At the very maximum, as the intensity of the con-tinuous spectrum further increases, the strongest hydrogen lines appear in absorption, as fuzzy and weak lines. If the star lingers at constant maximum brightness, the spec-trum remains unchanged; it starts to evolve backwards only when the star begins to fade. Thus the spectrum appears to vary along with the brightness of the variable. The maxi-mum intensity of the continuous spectrum shifts farther into the ultra-violet as the brightness of the star increases. In general, the U Geminorum stars are definitely bluish-white in color. The photographic amplitudes of these stars are only slightly in excess of the visual ranges.

Although the hydrogen lines and a few lines of higher atomic excitation, such as those of neutral and ionized helium, are present in the spectra of the U Geminorum stars, the general aspect of the spectrum corresponds to a much lower energy of excitation than that of a normal nova at maximum. The general behavior of the spectrum, however, recalls to mind that of the novae, in particular the fact that at maximum it is of the absorption type, and that it changes into an emission spectrum as the brightness of the star fades. Although the lines are fuzzy and the measures difficult, it seems that the velocities of expansion for the U Geminorum stars, which are of the order of one hundred kilometers per second, are much smaller than those observed in regular novae.

The connection between U Geminorum stars and novae is further emphasized by still another fact. As we have seen, fast U Geminorum stars, with cycles between ten and twenty days, have amplitudes around three magnitudes. Those with cycles between 50 and 70 days have a range of four magnitudes, while for those with still longer cycles, the range amounts to about five. The longer the interval, the bigger the burst! At this rate of change of amplitude with cycle-length, we should expect U Geminorum stars with cycles of 30 or 40 years to have an amplitude of eight or nine magnitudes. Now this amplitude is just about that of the recurrent novae, such as RS Ophiuchi and U Scorpii, which as far as we are aware, have exploded at intervals of 30 to 40 years. This correlation was pointed out a few years ago by Kukarkin and Parenago, and is highly significant.

If we try to fit ordinary novae into this scheme, then, from their average amplitudes of thirteen magnitudes, we might derive for them average cycles of 10,000 years or more. If the relation holds and the extrapolation is accepted, this might explain why most ordinary novae have not been observed to explode more than once.

A difference between U Geminorum stars and novae is found in their apparent distribution in the sky. Novae are usually found along the Milky Way, or not far from it, while U Geminorum stars, although more abundant in these regions, are also found in other parts of the sky. This difference, however, is not unique, since we find a similar discrepancy in distribution in the family of Cepheids.

U Geminorum stars are all extremely faint; the brightest among them, SS Cygni, appears of the twelfth apparent magnitude at normal minimum brightness. One cannot escape the conclusion that they are dwarfish stars and since their colors are white, they must be some variety of white dwarfs. From their annual motions in the sky, Kukarkin and Parenago conclude that they are probably intrinsically fainter than novae at normal brightness.

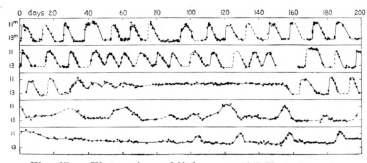

Fig. 67.—Five sections of light curve of RX Andromedae.

Z Camelopardalis Stars

The U Geminorum family as a whole is a rather queer family. We have, however, not yet made the acquaintance of its queerest members, the Z Camelopardalis stars. There are only a half dozen such objects, but they make up for their rarity through diversity of behavior. As a good example of what one of these stars can do, we present to our readers the five curves in Figure 67. They are not, as you may at first think, the light curves of five different variables, but five sections of the light curve of one star, RX Andromedae, at different epochs.

All Z Camelopardalis stars have ranges of about three magnitudes. When their variation is "regular"—and this

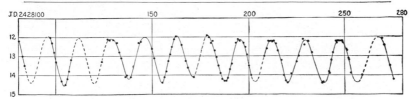

Fig. 68.—Light curve of CN Orionis 1935–1936.

does not happen too often—they behave very much like U Geminorum stars of short "period"; the only difference being that their permanence at constant minimum brightness is relatively shorter, and the amplitude of the variation somewhat smaller. Their cycles during these "regular" spells all fall between 13 and 22 days.

Although regular variations have been observed to continue for as long as a year or more in the two most representative stars, Z Camelopardalis and RX Andromedae, much of their time is spent in erratic fluctuations, during which the range of variation is considerably reduced. One of the strangest characteristics is that from time to time they take a sort of vacation, and remain at almost constant brightness. These vacations may last from a few weeks to many months, and at those times the brightness of the star appears to remain more or less approximately one-third of the way from maximum to minimum. Why just there, nobody knows; nor do we know why they take these vacations. The most leisurely member of the family seems to be TZ Persei, which remained at constant brightness during a whole year, without interruption.

Nothing was known about the spectra of Z Camelopardalis stars until recently, but now Elvey has shown that they do not differ, as far as their general aspect and behavior are concerned from those of ordinary U Geminorum stars.

Probably to be included in this group are two other stars, CN Orionis and AH Herculis, which are white in color and

undergo semi-regular variations of three magnitudes. Both
show a smooth light curve with no major irregularities. CN
Orionis (Figure 68) has an average period of 18 days, AH
Herculis, of 19 days. The reason why we believe these two
stars belong in the Z Camelopardalis group is the fact that Z
Camelopardalis and RX Andromedae often vary in this
special manner; also, there is no other place for them in our
listing of types.

Nova-like Variables

Our picture of exploding stars would not be complete if
we did not say a few words about some other variables that
show, or have shown in the past, behavior and physical
characteristics similar to those of the novae. The best known
nova-like variable is Eta Carinae, a star that now shines as
a quiet telescopic star of the eighth magnitude in a crowded
region of the Milky Way in the southern hemisphere, but
whose past is full of glorious splendor. The recorded history
of this star dates back to the end of the 17th century, when it
appeared as a star of the third or fourth magnitude. At the
middle of the 18th century, it was certainly brighter, of the
second or third magnitude; then it dimmed a little, but this
was only a temporary decline, because the greatest display
was yet to come. Around 1835 Eta Carinae boldly increased
to the rank of the first magnitude stars, and with slow oscillations, finally reached a peak in 1843 at magnitude -1,
becoming the second brightest star in the sky, exceeded only
by Sirius. It remained brighter than the first magnitude
until 1858, when it began a steady decline, and by 1865
it became too faint to be seen with the unaided eye (Figure
69). During the last forty years its brightness has been practically constant, of the eighth magnitude. Nothing is known
about the spectrum of Eta Carinae when it was a brilliant
star. Today it shows an emission spectrum not unlike that of

Nova Herculis in the latest stages of its first, rapid decline. In 1890, during a secondary maximum, when Eta Carinae had brightened to more than the seventh magnitude, a strong continuous spectrum was visible, crossed by many absorption lines.

A peculiar group of six variables, of which Z Andromedae is the best known, is also affiliated with novae. They are normally red stars, with M-type spectra, and they show slow

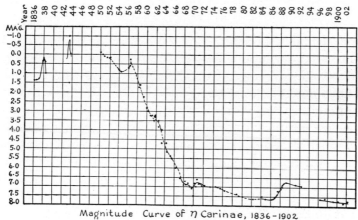

Magnitude Curve of η Carinae, 1836–1902

Fig. 69.—Light curve of Eta Carinae 1836–1902.

(*Innes*)

semi-regular, or irregular, fluctuations of small amplitude, not dissimilar to those of α Orionis and other M-stars. At times, however, they suddenly increase by about three magnitudes, and on these occasions the M-type spectrum is over-powered by that of a hot, blue star with nova characteristics, which shows that we probably are dealing here with a system of two stars which influence each other by some mysterious inter-action. The increase in brightness and the subsequent decline, with oscillations, is much slower than in ordinary novae. When the star has again become

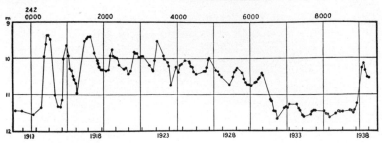

Fig. 70.—Light curve of Z Andromedae 1912–1939.
(*Prager*)

faint, the nova spectrum, which in the meantime has shown a nova-like evolution, disappears. Z Andromedae (Figure 70) "exploded" in the years 1901, 1914, and 1940.

One more variable star, probably related to novae, is V Sagittae, an active variable with a range of four magnitudes, in whose erratic variations two periods, one of 17 days, and the other of 530 days, are sometimes discernible. Its spectrum, which is continuous, with the greatest strength in the ultra-violet region, shows a few helium emission lines. Its variations, as C. Payne-Gaposchkin suggests, recall somewhat those of Nova Persei 1901 after return to normal minimum, and it is not improbable that V Sagittae was actually a regular nova sometime in the past.

Thus have we arrived at the end of our story about explosive stars. In view of their temperamental character, you must agree that they play a somewhat dramatic role in the field of stars that vary. Although we have by no means learned the real causes which produce them, yet we have been able to peer into some of the factors which govern their actions and to show how, if not exactly why, they explode and produce such spectacular and remarkable aspects.

7

ERRATIC STARS

WE HAVE IN THE CHAPTER ON RED VARIABLES ALREADY made the acquaintance of stars that vary irregularly. There it was shown that the red, irregular variables were linked up with the semi-regular, red stars, and the long-period, Mira stars. We have also mentioned in another chapter, the rather irregular variables of the U Geminorum and Z Camelopardalis types, which, because of their peculiarities, were grouped with the explosive stars.

In this chapter we shall treat those variable stars which appear to be totally irregular, not only in range of light variation, but also in the frequency of their cycles of change; stars which can not well be included in the three main families of intrinsic variables. These erratic variables, as we shall designate them, appear to fall into four separate groups, although it is not to be understood that these stars are closely related in any way.

R Coronae Borealis Stars

If you had started to observe R Coronae Borealis when at maximum in the summer of 1925, with the expectation of soon noting a decided decrease in light, as happened with one of the authors, your patience would have been sorely tried. In fact at that time, and for nearly ten years following, the brightness of the variable remained practically constant, at the sixth magnitude, close to naked-eye visibility. R Coronae Borealis is not a variable with a small range in brightness; on the contrary, when it does decrease in light, it may sink for nine magnitudes, exceeded in range only by some of the novae. Although R Coronae Borealis has the general habit of remaining at nearly constant brightness for most of the time, it does, without the least warning, drop hurriedly to a minimum, at almost any magnitude between 6.5 and 15. As a rule the star remains at minimum for a few

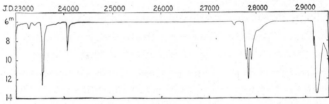

Fig. 71.—Light curve of R Coronae Borealis 1921–1939.

months, or a year or more, but it has been known to remain in an abnormal state, below its usual maximum brightness, for ten years. While the drop to minimum is usually very sudden—at times decreasing some seven magnitudes in a month—the recovery is usually slow, accompanied by very marked fluctuations, before the star attains normal, maximum brightness again. The variations are illustrated in Figure 71.

It is difficult to find a perfect regularity among natural phenomena, for there are always some perturbing factors to spoil the regularity. Even the most regular variables, the Cepheids, undergo slight changes in period as well as in shape of their light curves. Yet it is perhaps still more difficult to find a completely irregular phenomenon, since al-

most every natural event follows some statistical rule.
The fluctuations of the irregular, red variables are confined
within certain limits, and we may determine for them a
"most probable" length of cycle, and amplitude of variation.

A few years ago the light curve of R Coronae Borealis was
used as a subject for a statistical investigation by T. E.
Sterne, who found that this particular star is really an
"ideal," irregular variable, with not only completely irregular amplitudes of variation in light, but one for which
the times of minimum are distributed absolutely at random,
according to the laws of pure chance.

There are only about a dozen variables which can, with
certainty, be classed as R Coronae Borealis stars. Those
for which spectra are known belong to Classes *G* and *R*,
with super-giant characteristics. R Coronae Borealis itself
is classed as *G*0, which, were it not for the presence of some
peculiar spectral lines, would make it appear very similar to
a classical Cepheid. The peculiar lines to which we refer are
due to an excess of carbon in the atmosphere of the star.
According to L. Berman the atmosphere of R Coronae
Borealis is composed of 67 per cent carbon, 27 per cent
hydrogen, and the remaining six per cent of light metals
and other elements.

We find in this extraordinary abundance of carbon a very
plausible explanation for the variation in light of R Coronae
Borealis stars. Berman and O'Keefe think that the role
which carbon plays in the atmospheres of these stars is
much like that of water vapor in the Earth's atmosphere.
Under normal conditions the carbon would be vaporized
and thus made transparent to the radiation from the star's
surface. As water vapor in our own atmosphere condenses to
water droplets, or solid ice crystals, thus forming opaque
clouds, so can we imagine that a slight variation in temperature, or some other cause, would produce a similar con-

densation in the carbon vapor of the R Coronae Borealis stars. Thus it can readily be seen what the resulting condition on stars would be. The carbon, as one of the most opaque of substances, would need to produce only a very thin veil around the star in order to cut off enough light to make the star itself seem to almost disappear.

All R Coronae Borealis stars show a large range in total brightness, between five and nine magnitudes. One of the most interesting of these stars, RY Sagittarii, shows, in addition to its large erratic fluctuations, a semi-regular variation of about half a magnitude, with an average periodicity of 39 days. These superposed fluctuations, with a period and range of magnitude typical for long-period Cepheids (although the latter are much more uniform) are of further interest because the spectrum of RY Sagittarii, as for R Coronae Borealis, shows many features common to the spectra of classical Cepheids. R Coronae Borealis stars and Cepheids, in spite of their radically different behavior, may have more in common than we would at first have expected.

Nebular Variables

The vast space between the stars is by no means empty. Especially near the plane of the Milky Way we find much evidence of diffuse, irregularly distributed masses of cosmic dust, which must produce a dimming effect on the light of the stars which lie beyond. Sometimes these patches of cosmic dust, or dust clouds, are close enough to bright stars to reflect their light and then become visible as diffuse nebulosities. The spectroscope reveals that the nebulous material is composed not only of small particles but also of gases that become luminous under the influence of the radiation of hot, nearby stars.

In some of these regions where the nebulous material, whether dark or bright, is particularly dense, we find variable stars in abundance. The variations of such stars are usually erratic and of a peculiar nature, obviously suggesting that the cause of the fluctuation in light lies in the nebulosity, rather than in the stars themselves. Nearly a hundred irregular variables have been found within the confines of the Great Orion Nebula, and some fifty others in that region are suspected of variability. Other groups of irregular variables are found in, or near, other bright nebulous regions, as for example in the regions of Eta Carinae, the Pleiades, and also in the patch of dark nebulosity in Corona Austrina.

These "nebular" variables usually display rather small fluctuations, of the order of one or two magnitudes, but

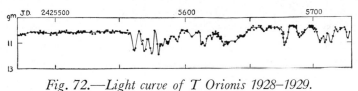

Fig. 72.—Light curve of T Orionis 1928–1929.

frequently much less, and they show a definite tendency to remain longer at maximum light than near minimum brightness. One of the best known of these nebular stars is T Orionis, usually of the tenth magnitude, but often decreasing to the eleventh or twelfth magnitude; it is found at the sharp edge of a wing in the giant "Bat-like" figure of the Orion Nebula. On occasion, T Orionis remains at almost constant brightness for two or three months, but more frequently its light variations are a succession of rapid, irregular fluctuations. Sometimes the decreases to minimum brightness require but a few days and are followed by more gradual increases which are interrupted by a fading away again before another period of apparent calm has been reached. Whether or not these sudden drops to minimum are simply the result of a temporary cutting off of the light of the star caused by the passing of dust clouds between us and the star still requires investigation; it is not easy to explain the more rapid decreases to minimum by simple occulting. It is very probable that the relation between nebulosity and stellar variation is of a complex nature. Perhaps part of the explanation may lie in the effect of the nebulosity upon the atmospheres of the stars themselves. The erratic variations of T Orionis are shown in Figure 72.

T Orionis is, perhaps not typical as regards the behavior of nebular stars; its fluctuations seem to be much more rapid than those found in the average nebular variable. Generally, it is very difficult to obtain complete and reliable light curves for this type of variable, mainly because of the uncertainty encountered in estimating the brightness of an object enmeshed in nebulosity. Some variables, such as R Monocerotis, R Coronae Austrinae, and RY Tauri, appear to be located at the tip-end of small fan-like nebulae, resembling a comet with the star as head. The nebulae themselves appear to fluctuate in brightness as the star varies. It is not yet clear whether the variations found in such systems of star and associated nebula represent the same phenomenon as those we find for the irregular variables in the large diffuse nebulae. The available data are still too scanty to allow us to decide whether or not we have to deal here with one or two distinct kinds of variables. The R Monocerotis nebula is shown in Figure 73.

Nebular variables belong generally to spectral classes *B*, *A*, and *F*. In their spectra are found some peculiar bright lines, the presence of which can be explained by the excitation of the surrounding nebular gases. Some white variables, such as BN Orionis, WW Vulpeculae, YZ Cephei, and VX Cassiopeiae, with no visible nebulosity around them, show variations that closely resemble those found for the known nebular variables, and should probably be classed with

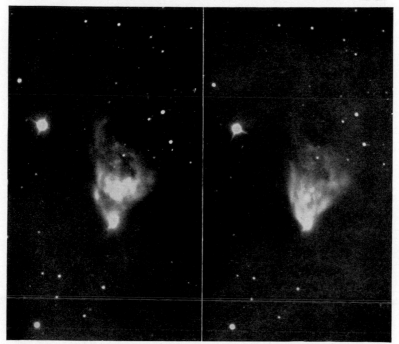

Fig. 73.—Hubble's variable nebula associated with R Monocerotis.

The variable star is at the lower tip of the nebula. (*Photographs made with the 100-inch telescope at the Mount Wilson Observatory, September 18, 1920 and November 1, 1921.*)

them. YZ Cephei, in particular, shows extremely rapid variations in light, interrupted by constant maxima which are similar to those observed in T Orionis.

VARIABLES OF THE RR TAURI GROUP

The variables of the rapidly varying, erratic type, typified by RR Tauri, are relatively few in number and show a considerable range in magnitude. In RR Tauri itself, sudden changes in light amounting to two or three magnitudes frequently occur within a few days, while at other times the

changes are small and decidedly slow. RW Aurigae varies so
rapidly that it has been difficult to obtain a reliable light
curve in spite of the combined efforts of several observers.
Its variations appear to consist of two sorts of irregular
waves, one with a length of a few days, the other of several
months. The variations of RR Tauri are shown in Figure 74.

The spectra for RR Tauri, RY Orionis, and UX Orionis
are not known, but we do know that RW Aurigae is a yellow star of spectral type G0. All four of these stars are yellow in color, and they present similar variations in light.
Two other variables of the same sort, SY Cancri and CO

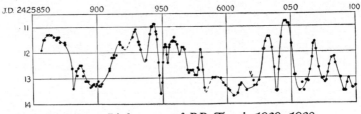

Fig. 74.—Light curve of RR Tauri, 1929–1930.

Orionis, with large amplitudes, are definitely white in color.
It is difficult to say whether or not these objects, so few in
number, represent a distinct, homogeneous group of variables. The Gaposchkins suggest that the RR Tauri stars may
be related to the nebular variables.

Probably related to the RR Tauri stars are RY Bootis and
UY Aurigae. The former, with a variable spectrum of class
F, has a total range in light variation of only half a magnitude, and although the variations are, in general, small and
irregular, they show, at times, traces of a nine-day periodicity. UY Aurigae, which has a *G*-type spectrum, and which is
located in a heavily obscured region, exhibits frequent
fluctuations in what appears to be cycles of nineteen days,
but then again, at times, not the slightest evidence of

regularity prevails and the light curve becomes a veritable jumble.

Gamma Cassiopeiae and P Cygni Stars

Gamma Cassiopeiae, the central star of the five which form the well-known "W" of Cassiopeia's Chair, was, until 1936, believed to be non-variable. Its spectrum is what is known as a very "early" type, $B0$, and it shows peculiar, bright hydrogen lines, each line being split into two components by a dark absorption line in the center. This type of spectrum is not common, although there are known to exist more than four hundred stars with the same characteristics.

There is no doubt that between the years 1890 and 1910 the brightness of γ Cassiopeiae was practically constant, at magnitude 2.25, about the same as Polaris, the Pole Star. In 1936 a marked increase in the brightness of γ Cassiopeiae was noted, amounting to at least half a magnitude, and until April 1937 its brilliance had further increased to a maximum of 1.6, only slightly less brilliant than α Cygni. Almost immediately the light of the star began to decrease at a moderately rapid rate until, in November of that year, it had reached its normal magnitude of 2.25. But, curiously enough, it was not content to remain at the magnitude which had prevailed for so many years, and the star continued to decrease in brilliance until, in 1940, it had faded to the third magnitude, see Figure 75.

Accompanying these light variations there were also variations in the spectrum of the star. Before 1932, no appreciable spectral changes had been noted, but in the spring of that year the aspect of the double, bright, hydrogen lines changed considerably; while one of the two components gradually grew fainter, the other became relatively brighter. Later this condition was reversed, and the component which was at first the fainter, finally exceeded in intensity that of

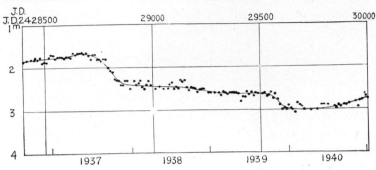

Fig. 75.—Light curve of Gamma Cassiopeiae.

the other. It is very probable that the light variations started when the spectral changes began, but they apparently were not conspicuous and we have no record of any variations in light until 1936. At the time of maximum light, the absorption lines in the spectrum appeared strong, but when, in 1938, the star had diminished in light, these absorption lines had weakened and the bright emission lines had become relatively stronger. It may be recalled that a similar behavior of the bright and dark lines is observed in the novae, although the spectrum of γ Cassiopeiae can not be said to resemble that of a nova.

Merrill and Miss Burwell suggested, some years before the variability of γ Cassiopeiae was discovered, that the spectra of most *B*-type stars with bright lines are variable. McLaughlin points out that the one particular characteristic of these spectral variations is the long interval—perhaps a century or more—of almost complete inactivity, broken by short periods of activity during which times semi-periodic spectral changes, that last for several years, are recognizable.

Other *B*-type stars with bright-line spectra which were previously known to vary are Phi and X Persei. A few others have been found recently, among them BF Cygni, which has a range in light variation of about four magnitudes. It is possible that all *B*-stars with bright lines, if carefully observed over many years, would show signs of variability.

A group of stars which probably are closely allied to stars similar to γ Cassiopeiae are the so-called "P Cygni" stars. These stars show spectra with a continuous background, not unlike the *B*-stars, in which the lines of hydrogen, helium, and ionized oxygen are present, both as dark absorption and bright emission; the bright lines are always to the red side of the dark lines. P Cygni itself, now a star of the fifth magnitude, has in the past displayed a behavior not far different from that of γ Cassiopeiae. Twice during the seventeenth century P Cygni increased in brightness to the third magnitude. This star has often been called "nova-like," but its giant characteristics—most P Cygni stars are probably on the average 10,000 times more luminous than ordinary novae at their normal, minimum brightness—make it difficult to place it in the sequence of the dwarfish explosive stars. Of the dozen or so stars with P Cygni spectra, several are known to be variable stars.

It has been suggested that the variations in such stars as γ Cassiopeiae and P Cygni may be due entirely to changes occurring in the higher levels of the stars' atmospheres, where the bright lines supposedly originate. But the marked changes in the absorption lines, accompanied by rather large light variations in some of these stars, seem to favor the idea that the changes involve somewhat deeper levels, including the actual surfaces or photospheres of the stars.

It certainly is remarkable that the changes in the intensities of the dark and bright lines in the spectra of P Cygni stars show some analogy to the changes in the spectra of novae. We must not forget, however, that, just like novae, these stars are very hot and that the strong ultra-violet radiation may well produce similar reactions in the surrounding atmospheres, even though the internal structures of the stars may be radically different. Accordingly, it is yet too early to propose that the early spectral type variables, such as γ Cassiopeiae and P Cygni, are related to novae.

8

STELLAR ECLIPSES

Up to this point in our story, we have dealt almost exclusively with the stars that are inherently variable; that is, with those stars which go through their light variations as the result of physical changes in the stars themselves. But there is a class of variables which does not change in light through any internal causes. These stars neither contract nor expand, they do not change their temperature, nor do they vary because of changing conditions in their atmospheres. In other words, when they vary in light, it is only because of effects resulting from their geometrical positions as viewed from the Earth. As seen from other positions in space many of these same stars would appear to be of constant brightness; while some others, now considered as nonvariable, would appear to be variable. Such stars are known as eclipsing binaries.

If you scan the sky with the aid of a telescope, you will soon notice that not all stars appear single. Often a star which looks like any other star, when observed with the naked eye, appears in the telescope to be actually composed of two stars in close proximity. Frequently the two stars are white and approximately of the same brightness, but in a good many instances the pair is composed of a bright reddish star and a fainter companion which, by contrast, appears blue or greenish. Colored double stars of this sort present some of the most beautiful telescopic sights. Objects such as β Cygni, α Herculis, and γ Andromedae are well known to all enthusiastic star gazers.

Sometimes the proximity of two stars is only apparent. One of them lies much closer to us than the other, and it is only by chance that we observe them as double stars. These are generally referred to as optical doubles. More often the two stars are actually physically associated in space, held together by the force of gravitation which causes them to revolve about each other. These are known as binary stars. Sometimes such "physical star systems," so named in contrast to those in which the nearness is only apparent, contain also a third star; even quadruple and quintuple stars have been observed.

More than twenty thousand double and multiple stars have been discovered by telescopic observations. In many cases the components of a binary star take centuries to revolve around each other, but in other instances their periods of revolution amount to only a few decades. The shortest known period is that of the star BD $-8°4352$ recently discovered by Kuiper, which requires only a year and eight months to complete a revolution. This, however, is by no means the shortest period possible for a binary star. Pairs with short periods are usually nearer together than those which revolve slowly. The reason why we do not observe visually double stars with periods shorter than a year, is that our telescopes are not powerful enough to separate the components.

To detect double stars that revolve more rapidly, we have to make use of our good old friend the spectroscope. If a star is double, no matter how close the two components are, it

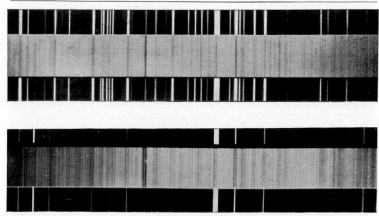

Fig. 76.—Two spectra of the spectroscopic binary Zeta Ursae Majoris (Mizar).

In the lower spectrum all lines appear double. Above and below each spectrum of the star a laboratory iron arc spectrum is shown for comparison.

will show two superimposed spectra. When the two spectra differ considerably, it will not be difficult for the experienced astronomer to disentangle them; the troubles begin when the stars are twins, with identical spectra. The astronomer has, however, a detective in the Doppler effect. As the two components move in their orbits, the velocities in the line of sight will change. Consequently the whole set of lines of one spectrum will shift with respect to the set of lines in the other spectrum, and both sets will swing back and forth in the period of revolution of the system. (Figure 76.)

By watching the change in position of the spectral lines, the period of revolution of any binary star can be determined. Some of these "spectroscopic" binaries, as such stars are called, have periods of several years, comparable with those of the shortest visual binaries, but most of them revolve much faster and periods of a few days, or even less than a day, are not unusual.

ECLIPSING BINARIES

Under special circumstances a double star, for which the components are so close that they cannot be separated telescopically, can be detected without the aid of the spectroscope. This condition prevails when the orbital plane of the pair lies very nearly in our line of sight; the two components are then bound to pass one in front of the other at every half revolution. What the result will be can be readily imagined from what occurs when the Moon passes in front of the Sun during a solar eclipse. Part, or sometimes all, of the light coming from the eclipsed component of the star will be cut off and we therefore observe an apparent drop in the total brightness of the system. Our double star will then have become a variable star. Although the light variations of eclipsing binaries are only of a geometrical nature, these stars are included among the variables.

Imagine a system of two spherical stars in which the components are exactly equal in size and brightness, and which revolve in an orbit lying exactly in our line of sight. In such an ideal case we will have at each revolution two identical eclipses, during which, for a short time, one star will completely disappear behind the other. The total brightness will drop during the eclipses by fifty per cent, which corresponds to 0.75 magnitudes. The light curve of such a system will consist for each revolution, of two equal minima, 0.75 magnitudes in depth, separated by intervals of constant maximum brightness (see Figure 77a).

The foregoing is an idealized condition. The components of an eclipsing binary will in general differ in size and brightness, their orbits will not lie exactly in the line of sight, and the shapes of the stars will not be perfectly spherical, because of their mutual gravitational attraction. We observe, therefore, a great variety of eclipses. As you may

recall, a solar eclipse may be total, when the Moon's diameter appears equal to, or larger than that of the Sun; or
annular, when the Moon is unusually far away, and its
smaller disk is not sufficiently large to cover that of the Sun,
so that the rim of the Sun will shine as a ring around the dark
lunar disk. In addition, we may have all sorts of partial
eclipses, from a small notch in the Sun's face to almost total

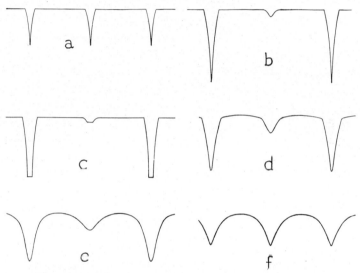

Fig. 77.—Typical light curves of eclipsing variables.

coverage, when a tiny crescent is all that remains of the Sun.
But the apparent diameters of the Moon and Sun do not
differ greatly, whereas in binary stars we have all sorts of
possible ratios between diameters of the components. In
addition, the picture will be further complicated by the fact
that the occulting companion is not perfectly dark, as is the
Moon during solar eclipses.

Let us first consider what happens when the components
of the binary system differ in brightness. We shall then,

obviously, observe a greater loss of light when the darker
component hides the brighter one, than when the latter cuts
off the dimmer light of its companion. The result will be a
light curve with unequally deep minima, see Figure 77*b*.
If the darker star is the larger—which almost invariably
happens—the brighter star may remain totally eclipsed for
some time, and during that time the brightness of the system
will remain constant at minimum light. Thus, total eclipses
will be ear-marked by light curves with very flat minima
(Figure 77*c*). If the primary eclipse is total, then the secondary eclipse must be annular, and should show a constant
brightness during the time that the smaller star remains
projected upon the larger, at least if the surface brightness
of the larger star were constant from center to edge.

If the two stars are sufficiently close to each other, then,
under the influence of their mutual attraction, their shapes
will be distorted into oblate figures, called ellipsoids, see
Figure 78. The extremities of
these ellipsoids should always
point toward the center of
gravity of the system, and
they should, therefore, rotate
once around their axes during each revolution; as a
result, the stars present to the

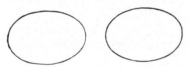

*Fig. 78.—A system of two
stars elongated into ellipsoids by
gravitational distortion.*

observer a continually changing apparent area. The apparent area is largest, and the two stars appear brightest when
the line joining the centers of the pair lies perpendicular to
the line of sight, that is mid-way between eclipses. The brightness of the system does not remain constant between eclipses,
as is shown by Figure 77*d*. If the stars are considerably
elongated, the light curve will appear still more rounded, as
illustrated in curve *e*. In the special, but frequently observed,
instance of ellipsoidal components of equal brightness, the

light curves will present two minima of equal depth, as is shown in curve *f*.

TYPES OF ECLIPSING VARIABLES

The stars whose light remains sensibly constant between eclipses (curves *a*, *b*, *c*) are usually called variables of the Algol type, after the well-known star Algol, or Beta Persei. Those eclipsing variables with minima of different depth (curve *e*)—with elongated components—are called Beta Lyrae stars, and finally, the systems whose components are much elongated and are of equal or nearly equal brightness, with periods less than a day and a half, (curve *f*) are called W Ursae Majoris stars. Of course, not all eclipsing variables adhere strictly to the definitions of each type, and we may have light curves, such as the one represented by curve *d*, which belong half-way between the Algol and the Beta Lyrae types. When this condition occurs, the assignment to one or the other type is a matter of personal preference.

As we would expect for systems in which the stars are close together, Beta Lyrae and W Ursae Majoris stars have, on the average, shorter periods than the Algol stars. W Ursae Majoris stars have the shortest periods, ranging from 0.219 days (BP Pegasi) to 1.327 days (DW Carinae), with the most common period around 0.48 days. About 120 variables belong to this class, which represents eleven per cent of the total number of all eclipsing variables for which both period and type are known. The Beta Lyrae stars, which number about 140, are found most frequently to have periods around 0.8 days, but their range in period is considerable, from 0.48 days (BS Vulpeculae) to 199 days (W Crucis).

The great majority of eclipsing binaries are Algol variables, numbering nearly 800, or 73 per cent of the whole. Their most frequent period is somewhere between two and three days. The shortest period among eclipsing variables—

0.197 days, or 4 hours and 43 minutes—is that of the Algol variable, UX Ursae Majoris. The longest period—9883 days, or 27 years—is that of Epsilon Aurigae, also of the Algol type. There are, however, only 13 eclipsing variables with periods longer than 100 days, and only four of these periods exceed 1000 days.

DIFFERENT AMPLITUDES

The observed amplitude of an eclipsing variable depends, to some degree, on the method by which the star is observed, whether visually, photographically, or photoelectrically. Let us take as an example the system of Zeta Aurigae. This system consists of a comparatively small bluish-white component with a very bright surface, which is periodically eclipsed by a giant reddish component of low surface brightness, with a diameter 70 times as large as that of the smaller component. When observed on ordinary photographic plates, the amplitude at primary eclipse amounts to three quarters of a magnitude, which corresponds to a loss of half the total light of the system. This means that, as photographed, the two stars have the same total brightness; the larger size of the darker star exactly compensating for its lower surface brightness. The eye is more sensitive to red light than the ordinary photographic plate, so that the larger star will appear brighter when observed visually. Thus, when the smaller star is eclipsed, more than half of the total visual light of the system remains and the visual amplitude is less than 0.75 magnitudes. Actually, visual observations of Zeta Aurigae give a range in brightness of only 0.12 magnitudes. The use of an ultra-violet filter will, on the contrary, reduce the brightness of the larger component and accordingly deepen the minimum in the light curve; the amplitude so observed may, in fact, become two magnitudes for a special plate and filter combination.

If we observe a diminution of the amplitude at primary eclipse as we change from photographic to visual observations, we should obviously record a corresponding increase in the amplitude at secondary eclipse. When the two components do not differ very much in size, but are of decidedly different color, it may even happen that in proceeding from one method of observation to the other the secondary minimum of the light curve becomes deeper than the primary.

Of course, when there is no difference in color between the two components, the amplitudes at both eclipses remain the same, whatever method of observation is used. Such a condition prevails, for example, for most of the W Ursae Majoris stars, whose components are generally of approximately equal size, brightness, and color. Beta Lyrae stars show only slight differences, when observed photographically and visually, but for Algol stars the observed differences in amplitude are sometimes enormous. Thus, in any statistical study of amplitudes for an eclipsing binary, the material should be rigorously homogeneous, either all amplitudes photographic or all visual.

The average amplitude of a W Ursae Majoris variable is 0.65 magnitudes. If the components were spherical, we would not expect to find amplitudes greater than 0.75 magnitudes, but on account of their elongation, amplitudes as large as one magnitude are sometimes recorded. It may be remarked that two ellipsoidal components of a binary star revolving around each other would produce variation of the total brightness of the system, even if their orbital plane were so inclined to the line of sight that no eclipse could actually occur, because the apparent area of the two disks would vary continually as the ellipsoids rotate. Such systems have actually been observed; they are referred to as "Ellipsoidal" variables. Their detection, however, is extremely difficult because the amplitude in brightness is very small, hardly exceeding two tenths of a magnitude. Naturally if the two components happen to revolve in a plane exactly perpendicular to the line of sight, there would be no observable variation in light. Examples of ellipsoidal variables are b Persei and ζ Andromedae.

Beta Lyrae stars have amplitudes which, when observed visually, rarely exceed 1.5 magnitudes; this means that in such systems the difference in brightness between the two components is not very large. All possible amplitudes are recorded, on the other hand, among Algol stars. As we have already mentioned, the largest amplitude so far observed is that for CW Pegasi, which has a photographic range of 4.3 magnitudes. This amplitude would probably be exceeded by that of WW Cygni, if observed photographically. Its visual amplitude is 3.7, but since the darker component is reddish, it has been shown that the photographic amplitude would probably be around five magnitudes. Because of its faintness, photographic observations have not yet been secured on WW Cygni at minimum.

Darkening of Limb and Reflection Effects

There are a few minor effects that slightly modify the shape of the light curves of eclipsing variables. One is the so-called "darkening at the limb," or the decreased brightness at the rim of a stellar disk relative to the brightness near the center. A photograph of the Sun (see Figure 79) shows that at the center the surface appears to be brighter than at the edge. The cause of this phenomenon is to be found in the absorption by the Sun's atmosphere. Light rays from different parts of the Sun's disk reach the observer through the solar atmospheric envelope, and those rays which come from the outer parts must traverse a larger portion of the envelope than those which come directly from the center; they are, therefore, more dimmed by absorption. The absorption is

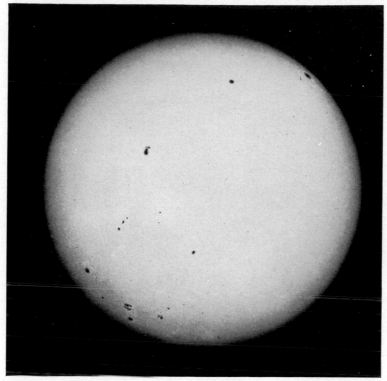

Fig. 79.—Photograph of the Sun showing "Darkening at the Limb."

more effective for blue rays than for yellow or red, and consequently, this darkening towards the limb of the Sun is more marked on ordinary photographs than when observed visually.

Stars are also darker at their edges, but the degree of darkening will vary, depending on the quality of the light emitted, and on the extent of the atmospheres. The effect of this limb darkening will show up during the progress of the eclipses, for it will slightly affect the shape of the light curve by smoothing off sharp angles at the beginning and at the end of the eclipse.

Another distorting factor is the "reflection effect." The light of each component is faintly reflected from the surface of the other, so that the hemispheres which face each other appear somewhat brighter than the two opposite hemispheres. When we have a small bright component with a large faint companion, the latter will act somewhat like a reflector in a flash-light. Therefore we will observe an increasing brightness due to reflection when the primary eclipse is over, and this increase will continue up to the moment when the companion is just behind the bright component, and the secondary eclipse begins. After the secondary eclipse, the extra light due to reflection will diminish. The light curve of Algol itself (see Figure 2) clearly shows this effect.

Physical Observations

Since eclipsing systems consist of two stars, or components, they should show in the spectroscope two superimposed spectra. Frequently only one spectrum is visible. This means that the second component is too faint to show under the observing conditions. When both spectra are visible the position of all the lines in the two spectra will swing back and forth around a mean position with a period equal to the period of revolution. Since the two stars are at opposite sides of the center of gravity, it necessarily follows that when one of them approaches the observer, the other recedes; thus the displacements of the spectral lines of the two components are always in opposite directions, see Figure 80.

If the two components have different masses, the lighter one will swing in a wide orbit, while the heavier one will keep closer to the center of gravity. Thus, if we observe that the radial velocity of one component varies over a larger

km/sec.

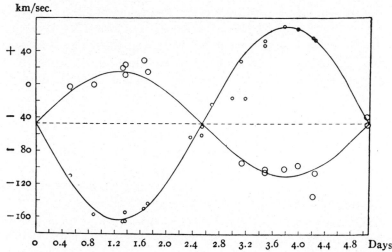

Fig. 80.—Radial velocity curve of RT Lacertae, according to Joy.

The larger circles represent the observed velocities of the fainter star and the smaller circles those of the brighter secondary star.

range than that of the second component, we can immediately conclude that the first star is the lighter component. The ratio of the amplitudes of the radial velocity curves for the two components will give us the ratio of their respective masses. If we are able to determine in some manner the total mass of the system, we automatically have the masses of the individual components.

WHAT STAR ECLIPSES REVEAL

We have seen that when the relative sizes, the distances between components, the surface brightnesses, the degree of ellipticity of the stars, and the inclination of the orbit are given in an eclipsing binary system, we can predict the form and amplitude of the light curve. We should also be able to use the inverse procedure and deduce the same facts from the light curve.

A first attempt in this direction was made by E. C. Pickering in 1880, followed by Hartwig in 1889, and Meyers in 1896. To the further development of the theory are linked the names of Pannekoek, Roberts, Rödinger, Blazhko, Stebbins, and Dugan. The most thorough attack of the problem was made in 1912–1913 by Russell who, in collaboration with Shapley, derived formulae and tables which are still in general use among computers of eclipsing variables. In more recent years Fetlaar, Sitterly and Krat have added still further to the solution of this problem, and refinements of procedure are currently being made by Wyse, Zessewitsch, Russell, and especially by Kopal.

When we have only the light curve at our disposal, we can not hope to deduce more than the relative elements of the system; that is, the dimensions and distances expressed in terms of the dimensions of one of the components, rather than in actual miles. We can go further though, if we also have available a curve of the observed radial velocities; and, if we are also fortunate enough to know the distance of the system, it becomes possible to compute almost everything we wish to know about the masses, diameters, temperatures, and other elements. Eclipsing variables prove to be especially valuable for our general knowledge of stellar masses; in fact they provide, together with the most rapidly revolving double stars, the only source of precise measures of the masses of the stars that the astronomer has today. To explain how these computations are made would be a lengthy undertaking and we shall limit ourselves to describing, in a few words, a rough picture of the technique that is now in use.

The light curve of an eclipsing variable tells us what fraction of the stellar disk is eclipsed at each moment. In general, there will be only one particular pair of stars, with a definite ratio of diameters, capable of producing the ob-

served light curve, and our first problem, a purely geometrical one, will be that of finding this ratio by trial and
error, with the aid of special formulae and tables computed
for the purpose. Next, we compare the duration of the
eclipses with the period of revolution and thus find the size
of the orbit in terms of the diameter of one of the components. The shape of the light curve will allow us to determine what fraction of one component is eclipsed by the other
at minimum light; and knowing the relative distance
between the stars, we can then obtain the inclination of the
orbit to the line of sight. The degree of ellipticity of the
components is also derived directly from the light curve in
the intervals between minima.

With these data at hand we are now ready to draw a
diagram of the system, with the sizes of the components and
the orbit proportionally correct. What we do not yet know is
the scale of our drawing, that is how many miles correspond
to an inch in our diagram. To determine this scale we have
to make use of the observed radial velocity curve when
available. We can read off the velocities in the line of sight
at different moments and, since we know the inclination
of the orbit, we can transform these values into true orbital
velocities. If the orbit is circular, the true velocity must be
constant, and by multiplying the true velocity by the length
of the period, we obtain the length of the orbit in miles, or
kilometers. If the orbit is an ellipse a mathematical step
called integration will be necessary, instead of the simpler
multiplication. Comparing the true length of the orbit with
that on our drawing, we obtain the desired scale and we can
then determine the diameters of our stars in miles.

The determination of the mass of the system requires the
application of Newton's law of gravitation and a comparison
with the Earth-Sun, or Earth-Moon, system. We know that
the Earth-Sun system, the mass of which we shall take as a

unit, has a period of revolution of 365 days and a separation of 93 million miles. The problem is first to find what mass our stars must have in order to revolve with their known period at the average distance that we have just determined. Kepler's third law of planetary motions, generalized on the basis of Newton's theory of universal gravitation, gives an immediate answer to the question.* If we wish to know the masses of the individual components, we have only to take, as has already been explained, the respective amplitudes of their radial velocity curves, and the ratios of these will yield directly the mass ratio of the two stars of the system.

If we also know the distance of the system, then we can determine the intrinsic brightness of each component and, by dividing the brightnesses by the area of the visible hemisphere, we can obtain the luminosity per unit of area. But this luminosity per unit area depends on the surface temperature and thus it follows that the temperature at the surface of the star can be obtained from orbital study as well as from a knowledge of the star's spectrum.

Eccentric Orbits

Double stars, with very short periods of revolution, usually have nearly circular orbits, but if we proceed to examine those with longer periods, we shall find more and more systems whose orbits are elongated ellipses. The same

---

* According to Kepler's third law, the cube of the major axis in any orbit in the universe must be proportional to the product of the square of the revolution and the total mass of the system. If we know the major axis of the orbits of both the Earth and the eclipsing system, we can immediately obtain the total mass of the stellar system in terms of that of the Earth-Sun system, which by the way is for all practical purposes equal to the mass of the Sun alone, as the Earth accounts for only 1/330,000th part of its value.

trend is observable in eclipsing binaries. The short-period W Ursae Majoris stars, as well as the Beta Lyrae variables, all have nearly circular orbits, but among the Algols, especially those with periods longer than three days, we find decidedly elliptical orbits.

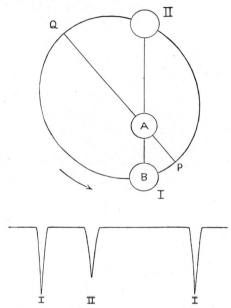

Fig. 81.—Eclipses in an eccentric binary system.
(Upper) diagram of orbit and resulting light curve (lower).

What is the effect of an elliptical orbit on the light curve of such a star? In the upper part of Figure 81 the orbit of star *B* is drawn with star *A* as stationary which is equivalent, for our purpose, to assuming that both *A* and *B* components are revolving around their common center of gravity. Eclipses occur when star *B* is at I or II; *P* is the periastron, or point of minimum distance between the stars; *PQ*, the major axis or "apsidal line" of the orbit; the direction of the motion is indicated by an arrow. Obviously it takes star *B* less time to pass from I to II than from II to I. Consequently, in the light curve the minimum corresponding to eclipse II must lie closer to the preceding minimum I than to the following minimum I, as is shown in the lower part of the figure. As star *B* moves faster at position I than at II, eclipse II should last longer than eclipse I, and if the ellipse is so eccentric that a change in velocity is noticeable even within the time interval of the eclipses, the ascending and descending branches of the curve will have a slightly different duration, which produces an asymmetry of the light curve at the times of eclipse. As a result of the ellipticity of the orbit, the radial velocity curve is also distorted.

If the apsidal line *PQ* does not remain fixed in space but instead rotates in the plane of the orbit, the interval of time between eclipses must change. Such changes have been observed for almost a dozen eclipsing stars. A typical example is that of the variable RU Monocerotis, with a period of 3.58 days. In 1901 its secondary eclipse occurred 2.69 days after the primary minimum, or 22 hours later than the mid-point between principal minima. In 1907 the delay of the secondary minimum had decreased to 21 hours; in 1914, to 19 hours; and in 1925, to 18 hours. The motion of the apsidal line is here very slow and computations show that about a thousand years will be required for the line of apsides to make a complete rotation. For some other stars the period of revolution is much shorter; Y Cygni, with a period of variation of three days, completes the whole revolution in 47 years and GL Carinae (Figure 82) in only 25 years.

Since the times of both the primary and the secondary minima are slowly changed by the rotation of the apsidal line, the period of the system will also appear to change if it

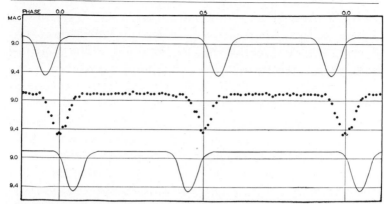

Fig. 82.—Apsidal motion in the system of GL Carinae, as revealed by the relative displacement of the primary and secondary minima.

(*H. H. Swope*)

is computed from primary minima alone. Therefore it is possible to detect the presence of an apsidal motion by examining the constancy of the period of light variation of the eclipsing system.

In attempting to find an explanation for apsidal motion we should remember that a rotation of the apsidal line is observed in the orbit of the Moon. Its period is about nineteen years and we know from celestial mechanics that this apsidal motion is due to two different causes: (1) the perturbing effect of a third body, in this instance the Sun; and (2) the irregularities of gravitational pull caused by the flattening of the Earth at the poles. As the Earth is only slightly flattened (the polar diameter is one third of one per cent smaller than that of the equatorial diameter) this second effect is practically negligible for the Moon. In close double stars, however, the flattening is very pronounced, and it may become of primary importance in apsidal motion. As yet no case has been found where the rotation of the apsidal line in eclipsing binaries could be

surely attributed to the presence of a third body in the
system, whereas there are several systems which show evidence of apsidal-motion due to flattening. The study of
such systems has led to some very interesting results.

Russell has shown that when the apsidal motion is due to
flattening, one has to consider whether the stars of the system
are of uniform density, or whether the material within the
stars is more condensed toward the centers, the magnitude
of the effect being smallest when the concentration is
greatest. If the masses of both stars are known then it is
possible to derive, from the speed of the apsidal motion, the
degree of concentration of the matter within. Since astronomers have no other means, except through pure theory, of
acquiring information concerning the distribution of matter
in the interior of a star, it is easily understood why these
by-products of the study of eclipsing binaries have been
hailed with so much enthusiasm. Unfortunately, less than
a dozen of these binaries have to date revealed apsidal
motions: Russell and Sterne are those who are mainly
responsible for what we know about this particular subject.

What leads us to exclude the idea that an observed
apsidal motion may be due to the presence of a third body in
the system? The chief objection is that this third body and
the eclipsing pair should revolve around their common center of gravity and, accordingly, we should observe a variation in the distance of the pair from us. This variation could
be detected in two ways: (1) spectroscopically by the Doppler line shift; (2) photometrically, since the time taken by
the light to reach us would vary as the distance varies and
thus a delay or an acceleration in the times of minima would
result. The presence of a third body has been suspected in
the systems of RT Persei, SW Lacertae, and VW Cephei
because of slight periodic variations in period that can not be
caused by a displacement of the apsidal line, since we find

that the relative positions of the primary and secondary minima remain unchanged.

Mention should be made here of other strange variations in period which have been detected, especially in recent times, in several eclipsing variables. As far back as 1888, discussing all the available observations of Algol made after 1782, Chandler concluded that the period of this star was subject to small changes of a rather complex character. He tried to represent the times of the observed minima by means of a complicated formula but this had to be replaced later by still another, because the first formula did not represent the more recent observations. The second formula failed again and finally Hartwig concluded that at least part of the variations in period were unpredictable, of an erratic nature. A similar erratic change in period was found much later to occur also in the Algol star U Cephei.

During the past few years a considerable number of eclipsing variables with irregularly varying periods have been added to the list, chiefly through the work of Dugan and Miss Wright based on the photographic material of the Harvard Observatory. The changes are usually very small, of the order of a few hundredths of a second; yet the accumulation of the small changes in period over several years produces delays and accelerations in the times of minima which may amount to three or four per cent of the length of the period. Quite exceptional is the star SV Centauri, for which the period has decreased by two full minutes in the last forty years. The period itself is 1.66 days. If the times of minima were predicted, starting from a minimum in 1900, with the period which prevailed at that time, the observed minima of 1941 would occur twelve days earlier than computed. Such a continual change in period, especially for an eclipsing variable, is a bit baffling. It has been suggested that the system of SV Centauri may be in a state of dynamical instability. A slight eccentricity in the orbit of the star may cause, through variations in attraction, a pulsation in one or both components with a period equal to the period of revolution. If this period happens to be the same, or nearly the same, as the period of free oscillation in the star, then a sort of resonance phenomenon may take place so that the pulsations would increase considerably in amplitude, and the continuous change in shape of the star would in turn affect the orbital motion.

PHYSICAL CHARACTERISTICS AND EXCEPTIONAL SYSTEMS

Eclipsing variables of the W Ursae Majoris type are dwarfs whose masses and temperatures are not very different from those of the Sun. In Beta Lyrae systems the components differ somewhat in size and brightness from each other; both are, as a rule, much brighter, much hotter, and much more massive than our Sun. As for Algol variables, practically all kinds and combinations of stars are possible. There are pairs of cool red dwarfs, such as RW Doradus and YY Geminorum (Castor C), as well as pairs of hot blue giants, such as Y Cygni and XX Cassiopeiae. UX Ursae Majoris is a splendid example of a system composed of tiny, but very dense, white dwarfs. Furthermore we find Algol systems, such as U Sagittae and WW Cygni, in which the brighter component is a normal white star and the companion is a fainter and cooler, but larger, giant. There are also others, such as Zeta Aurigae and VV Cephei, where normal white stars are eclipsed by monstrous red super-giant stars.

The systems of Zeta Aurigae and VV Cephei deserve special attention because of the peculiar conditions under which their eclipses occur. The apparent disk of the red component is, in both instances, many thousand times larger in area than that of the white one, so that the white star can be considered merely as a small, bright point, in comparison with the other. The atmosphere of the larger component is very much extended. As the time of eclipse approaches, the smaller star is at first veiled by this atmosphere and only after it has passed through deeper and deeper layers of this atmosphere and the occulting limb of the larger star is reached, does the actual eclipse begin. Consequently we shall observe in the combined spectra of the system more and more absorption lines due to the atmosphere of the eclipsing component. From these spectral variations we can learn about the composition, pressure, and temperature, at different heights in the atmosphere of the red star, a study which is impossible for all other stars except our Sun.

The period of Zeta Aurigae is 972 days and the first absorption lines produced by the atmosphere of the red star appear in the spectrum about thirty days before the real eclipse begins. This gives one some idea of the enormous extent of the atmosphere of the larger star. VV Cephei has a period of 7430 days—almost twenty years. Its eclipses occur so rarely that they become events of considerable astronomical importance, carefully watched for and studied by astronomers the world over.

Another star deserving special attention is Epsilon Aurigae, holder among eclipsing binaries of the record period of 9900 days, or 27 years. The amplitude of its light variation is 0.6 magnitudes. This value is practically the same, whether observed photographically or visually; a condition quite different from that of Zeta Aurigae whose amplitude, as we have already mentioned, varies from 0.1 to 2.1 magnitudes, depending on the method of observation. The light curve of Epsilon Aurigae is perfectly flat at minimum, which might indicate a total eclipse. If this were so, we would expect to see the spectrum of the eclipsed star disappear altogether, whereas it actually remains clearly visible throughout the duration of the eclipse. The smaller star is, obviously, not occulted by the larger star itself but passes through a semi-transparent shell which surrounds the larger star. Since the absorption is the same in the photographic as in the visual wave-lengths we must conclude that the shell is composed of small solid particles: in other words it must be something like a thin layer of cloud in the uppermost region of the star's atmosphere.

The real dimensions of these long-period eclipsing stars are enormous as compared with those of our Sun. The volumes of the larger components are, in units of the sun's volume, 12 billions for Epsilon Aurigae, 16 billions for VV Cephei, and 13 millions for Zeta Aurigae. In VV Cephei and Epsilon Aurigae the red component is slightly variable, with slow irregular fluctuations with a range of about 0.2 magnitudes. This fact makes a precise determination of the moments of beginning and ending of eclipse rather difficult.

Exceptional from another viewpoint is the system of UX Ursae Majoris. Its period of 4 hours and 43 minutes, as previously mentioned, is the shortest known among eclipsing variables. In order to revolve so rapidly, the components must be fairly close together. In spite of their closeness, however, no ellipsoidal distortion in the shape of the stars has been found; the brightness remains constant between the minima. The spectrum of only one component has been observed and it is of class *A*. It can be shown mathematically that the companion of a *normal A* star should, in order to revolve with a period shorter than five hours, actually move inside the star itself. Such a condition is, of course, impossible. In view of the fact that the components show no trace of gravitational distortion, we must conclude that their surfaces are fairly well separated from each other, and that they must be very dense and small. The brighter component is therefore not a normal *A* star; it is a white dwarf. The companion, whose spectrum is unknown but whose color is yellowish, must also be somewhat similar to a white dwarf.

The eclipses of UX Ursae Majoris last only about 40 minutes and the drop from maximum to minimum exceeds one magnitude. At the time of minimum the variations are so rapid that it requires a practically continuous watch if one desires to obtain a good light curve.

Eclipsing variables provide varied and interesting material for the investigator. So much valuable information can be obtained through their study that it is hardly necessary to emphasize the need for extensive observational material. In contrast, however, to most of the other types of variables, eclipsing stars are not particularly suitable for widespread cooperative work. Single isolated observations are of little value, especially if they do not possess a high degree of accuracy. For the determination of the light curves and their ultimate interpretation, extremely accurate observations are required. A few good photometric or photoelectric measures are vastly more valuable than many crudely made visual estimates. The routine observation of eclipsing variables during eclipse stages can, however, be productive of valuable results, if designed to determine accurately the times of minimum. This sort of work pertains more particularly to those Algol stars which vary through large amplitudes, and for which the astronomer needs to be kept well informed as to the time of the eclipse for his studies of apsidal motions and anomalous irregularities in period.

EPILOGUE

WE HAVE ARRIVED AT THE END OF OUR STORY OF Variable Stars. We have attempted to give a word picture of how the stars vary in light, of the types of variation which they present to us, of their spectral characteristics, and also something of the part they play in some of the problems of the universe. We have noted how Cepheids, for example, have been used as measuring rods to determine the size and shape of our own galaxy, as well as the distances to the external galaxies.

In the study of the eclipsing binaries we have shown what an important part they play in the determination of the sizes, the masses, and the densities of binary systems. We have also discussed their temperatures and their luminosities, and the motions in their orbits.

Although we have described at length many of the observed features of the Red Variables, especially those of long period, it can be safely said that there are numerous problems which are still not in the least understood; this, in spite of the many years of observation and research given to their study. Until we know more about what is going on inside the stars, as well as on their surfaces, the discovery of what causes them to vary, and why they present so many different forms of light curves, will remain a mystery. We hope that, when the clue or clues to these underlying causes have been found, there will be available a complete record of how the light has varied over these many, many years.

No less important would be the answer to the question as to why we have so many irregular variables—irregular, perhaps, only in the sense that at the present time we see no rhyme or reason in the manner of their variations. It may be that when we have solved the problems which they present, we shall find that they are in reality obeying laws that we had failed to discover.

Probably the most spectacular and exciting one of all has been the story concerning the history and development of the Exploding Stars, the Novae. In spite of their seeming frequency of occurrence, we still need more of them, and the appearance of other Novae will be looked forward to with great interest. When one does appear we must be prepared to tackle the problem of its thorough observation and analysis with all possible energy.

In variable stars doubtless lie many of the secrets concerning the universe as a whole. An unchanging world would tell us little, if anything, of what has happened in the past, of what is going on at present, and what may be expected to occur in the future. Only by the most diligent efforts on the part of the astronomer, both amateur and professional, in obtaining observational material and making intelligent discussion of this material can we ever hope to learn more, not only about our own immediate surroundings, but also about other stellar systems millions of light years distant.

The splendid example set for us by the various organizations of amateur variable star observers the world over merits our highest commendation and further encouragement. There is still a need for more of these groups, as well as for the augmentation of existing organizations. Variable star observing by visual and photographic methods still remains one of the most fruitful fields for the efforts of the amateur.

Observations without speculations, and speculations without observational facts to back them, will never get us far toward the solution of our problems. The amateur observer can perhaps best do his part by obtaining the necessary observations, leaving chiefly to the professional astronomer the task of analyzing the material and attempting to find acceptable explanations.

Let us refute the Emersonian declaration that, "The man in the street does not know a star in the sky."

ADDENDA

SPECTRA

AN ATOM CONSISTS OF A NUCLEUS, WHICH HAS A POSITIVE electric charge, around which revolve a number of much lighter, negatively charged corpuscles, called electrons. All electrons have the same mass and charge. Thus, the more electrons there are in an atom, the more charged and the more massive must be the nucleus in order that the atom itself shall be neutral. The properties of an atom depend largely on the nuclear charge. A neutral atom with only one electron revolving about it is called a hydrogen atom; one with two electrons, a helium atom; one with three electrons, a lithium atom, and so on to the heaviest known atom, that of uranium, which contains 92 revolving electrons. Through collision, or other causes, an atom may lose one or more of its electrons and thus remain positively charged. Such a mutilated atom is called an *ionized* atom.

If an atom is left undisturbed, all of its electrons will keep revolving in certain prescribed orbits. To each orbit there will correspond a definite total energy, and it can be shown that this energy is greatest for the electronic orbits with the largest radii. It frequently happens that through some external action an electron is forced to leave its usual path and swing in an orbit corresponding to one of higher energy. The atom which has thus acquired an additional amount

of energy is then said to be in an *excited* state. Under normal
conditions an atom can not remain in such an excited state
for as long as a millionth of a second. The displaced electron
will fall back to its former orbit, thereby releasing the
additional energy acquired in the process of excitation. The
energy is released by the atom in the form of a *quantum* of
radiation which travels through space with undulatory
motion at the rate of 186,000 miles per second.

Each atomic radiation has its own characteristic wave-
length. The shortest waves known belong to Gamma rays
and X-rays. Then, proceeding toward longer wave-lengths,
we find ultra-violet rays, light rays, heat rays, and radio
waves. There is a simple relation between the energy and
the wave-length of a radiation; the greater its energy, the
shorter its wave-length. Since the energy of a quantum of
radiation is determined by the difference between the
energies of the electron in the excited and in the normal
state, and since the possible number of excited orbits is
limited, and is characteristic of each element, it follows
that each atom can emit radiation of only certain determined wave-lengths.

An instrument called the *spectroscope* separates the various
wave-lengths of the light which passes through it. In a
spectroscope a narrow beam of strictly parallel light rays
is refracted as it enters a glass or quartz prism. Suppose that
we are dealing with sunlight, which is composed of almost
all possible individual rays, from those of short-wave violet
to the long-wave red rays. The short-wave rays are refracted
more than the long-wave rays. Therefore, when the light-
beam emerges from the prism, it is no longer composed of
parallel rays, but instead appears fan-like, with violet rays
at one end, red rays at the other, and the other colors distributed in between. If we interpose a screen in the path
of the refracted beam, we shall see projected upon it, a

strip of light with the colors of the rainbow. In this *spectrum* each point corresponds to a given wave-length.

In most spectroscopes the entering light-beam passes first through a narrow slit and then through a lens or system of lenses which brings the rays into parallelism before they reach the prism. The spectrum is either recorded on a photographic plate, or observed visually through a small telescope.

Kirchhoff's three laws describe the kinds of spectra that are observed:

1. An incandescent solid or liquid, or a gas under high pressure, emits a *continuous* spectrum, i.e., a spectrum in which all wave-lengths, from violet to red, are represented.

2. A glowing gas under low pressure radiates only in a few definite wave-lengths, thus giving a bright-line or *emission* spectrum.

3. If a gas capable of giving a bright-line spectrum is traversed by light originating from a hotter source it will absorb exactly those radiations which it would emit if it were glowing alone. Thus if we observe the continuous spectrum of a light bulb through a mass of sodium gas which is cooler than the filament of the bulb, we shall see it crossed by dark lines whose wave-lengths will be exactly equal to those of the bright lines that appear when the glowing gas is not traversed by any light. This type of spectrum is called an *absorption* spectrum.

When the rarefied gas referred to in Kirchhoff's second and third laws is composed only of atoms, the lines in the spectrum will appear mainly as single lines. When, on the other hand, the gas is composed of molecules, the lines will cluster in so-called *bands*, groups of lines sharply delimited on one side and gradually shaded off on the other. As molecules can not exist at very high temperatures, bands in stellar spectra are always indicative of comparatively low temperatures.

For each radiation, i.e., for each point in a spectrum, there is a corresponding definite wave-length. This wave-length is measured in Ångström units—one Ångström unit = 0.0000001 millimeters. A wave-length of 4386 Ångströms is usually expressed as λ4386.

The spectrum of a star is generally composed of a continuous background crossed by dark absorption lines. The light of the star originates from the hot, relatively dense photosphere, and reaches us after having traversed the somewhat cooler rarefied gases in the star's atmosphere. The continuous spectrum of the star is not uniformly intense. Red stars show a maximum intensity in the red portion of the spectrum, while blue stars show a maximum intensity in the blue or in the violet. It is known from laboratory experiments, and also from theory, that the wave-length corresponding to the maximum intensity in a continuous-background spectrum is dependent on the temperature of the light source—the hotter the source, the shorter the wave-length. Thus a blue star must be hotter than a red star.

In blue stars the absorption lines are mainly due to hydrogen and helium, while in yellow stars light metals, such as iron and calcium, are responsible for the main features of the absorption spectrum. This does not mean necessarily that the composition of the atmospheres of blue and yellow stars are radically different. It simply means that under the conditions of high temperature existing in the atmospheres of blue stars, all atoms of light metals are ionized and unable to absorb radiation in the visible part of the spectrum. Hydrogen and helium, on the other hand, require a high temperature for the production of absorption lines in the visible spectrum. Thus the general aspect of a stellar spectrum will be chiefly determined by the surface temperature of the star. According to their different aspects, stellar spectra have been divided into classes, which roughly follow a scale of surface temperatures. The main classes of the Harvard classification, now universally adopted, are the following:

1. Class *B*—Continuous spectrum strongest in the ultraviolet. Absorption lines of hydrogen and helium. Color of the stars: bluish-white. Temperature 22000°. (Rigel.)
2. Class *A*—Very strong hydrogen lines. *H* and *K* line of ionized calcium. Color: white. Temperature 11000°. (Sirius.)
3. Class *F*—Hydrogen lines weaker. *H* and *K* lines stronger than in class *A*. Faint lines due to light metals (iron, magnesium, etc.). Color: yellowish-white. Temperature 8000°. (Procyon.)
4. Class *G*—Hydrogen lines weak. *H* and *K* lines very strong. Extremely numerous narrow lines due to light metals. Color: yellow. Temperature 6000°. (Our Sun or Capella.)
5. Class *K*—Very strong metallic lines. λ4227 of neutral calcium prominent. Color: orange. Temperature 4000°. (Arcturus.)
6. Class *M*—Spectrum strongest in the red and infra-red. Strong titanium oxide bands. Numerous metallic lines. λ4227 very strong. Color: red. Temperature 3000°. (Antares.)

Less frequent, but highly important, are the following classes:

Class *O*—Very hot stars (surface temperatures from 30000° up). Continuous spectrum strongest in the far ultra-violet. Bright, wide lines of hydrogen, ionized helium, doubly and trebly ionized oxygen and nitrogen. The continuous spectrum is often very weak or almost entirely absent in the visible region of the spectrum. The bright lines in this type of spectrum and in other hot stars are due to the excitation of atoms in their atmospheres, by the strong ultra-violet radiation from their photospheres. (ζ Puppis.)

Class N—Continuous spectrum limited almost exclusively to the red and infra-red. Carbon and hydrocarbon compound bands. Color: ruby. Temperature 2000^0 to 3000^0. (19 Piscium.)

Class S—Similar to M; but with zirconium oxide bands predominant, instead of titanium oxide. (R Geminorum.)

Class R—Combining characteristics of classes K and N. Continuous spectrum and lines as in class K, but also strong carbon and hydro-carbon bands. (S Camelopardalis.)

Spectra of high-temperature stars are generally referred to as *early-type* spectra, while those of red stars are called *late-type* spectra. Therefore, it is quite common to say that a K star has a spectrum which is *later* than G, but *earlier* than M.

The Doppler Effect

When a light source approaches the observer, the eye will receive more waves per second than for the case where the light-source is at rest. Consequently the frequency of the vibrations will appear to be increased. An increase in frequency means a shift towards the violet end of the spectrum, and a decrease denotes a shift towards the red. Analogous to the theory of sound, we generally call this the

Doppler effect. If we notice that in a stellar spectrum all lines are shifted, say to the violet, we can safely conclude that the star, or at least the surface of the star, is approaching us. The amount of the shift is determined by the speed of approach or recession. If a star approaches at the velocity of 186 miles per second, which is exactly one thousandth part of the velocity of light, the apparent frequency of all its radiation will be increased by one tenth of one per cent. Since the wave-length equals the speed of light divided by its frequency, it is easy to convert an observed shift in wave-length into a velocity in the line of slight—measured in kilometers per second (Km/sec)—and called the *radial-velocity*.

Absolute Magnitudes

The apparent magnitudes of the stars do not tell us much about their real, intrinsic brightness because it is evident that the same star would appear of different brightnesses if observed from different distances. If we wish to establish a scale of real luminosities for the stars, we must imagine them as all brought to the same distance from us. Such a task is not too difficult if we are aware of the actual distances of our stars, because we know that the apparent brightness of light varies inversely as the square of its distance. Astronomers have chosen as a standard distance that of ten parsecs, or 32.6 light years. When the magnitude of a star is reduced to what it would be at this distance, it is called the *absolute magnitude*. If p is the parallax of the star and m its apparent magnitude, the absolute magnitude is computed by the formula:

$$M = m + 5 + 5 \log p$$

The term *parallax* is used to express half of the angular displacement of a star as seen from the earth when at opposite extremes of its orbit.

APPENDIX

α	Alpha	ι	Iota	ρ	Rho
β	Beta	κ	Kappa	σ	Sigma
γ	Gamma	λ	Lambda	τ	Tau
δ	Delta	μ	Mu	υ	Upsilon
ϵ	Epsilon	ν	Nu	ϕ	Phi
ζ	Zeta	ξ	Xi	χ	Chi
η	Eta	o	Omicron	ψ	Psi
θ	Theta	π	Pi	ω	Omega

CONSTELLATION ABBREVIATIONS

Name of Constellation	*Abbreviation*	*Genitive form of constellation*
Andromeda..................	And	Andromedae
Antlia.....................	Ant	Antliae
Apus......................	Aps	Apodis
Aquarius...................	Aqr	Aquarii
Aquila....................	Aql	Aquilae
Ara.......................	Ara	Arae
Aries.....................	Ari	Arietis
Auriga....................	Aur	Aurigae
Bootes....................	Boo	Bootis
Caelum....................	Cae	Caeli
Camelopardalis.............	Cam	Camelopardalis
Cancer....................	Cnc	Cancri
Canes Venatici.............	CVn	Canum Venaticorum
Canis Major...............	CMa	Canis Majoris
Canis Minor...............	CMi	Canis Minoris
Capricornus................	Cap	Capricorni
Carina....................	Car	Carinae
Cassiopeia.................	Cas	Cassiopeiae
Centaurus.................	Cen	Centauri
Cepheus...................	Cep	Cephei
Cetus.....................	Cet	Ceti
Chamaeleon................	Cha	Chamaeleontis
Circinus...................	Cir	Circini
Columba..................	Col	Columbae
Coma Berenices.............	Com	Comae Berenices
Corona Austrina............	CrA	Coronae Austrinae
Corona Borealis.............	CrB	Coronae Borealis
Corvus....................	Crv	Corvi
Crater....................	Crt	Crateris
Crux......................	Cru	Crucis
Cygnus...................	Cyg	Cygni
Delphinus.................	Del	Delphini
Dorado...................	Dor	Doradus
Draco....................	Dra	Draconis
Equuleus..................	Equ	Equulei

CONSTELLATION ABBREVIATIONS (*Continued*)

Name of constellation	*Abbreviation*	*Genitive form of constellation*
Eridanus	Eri	Eridani
Fornax	For	Fornacis
Gemini	Gem	Geminorum
Grus	Gru	Gruis
Hercules	Her	Herculis
Horologium	Hor	Horologii
Hydra	Hya	Hydrae
Hydrus	Hyi	Hydri
Indus	Ind	Indi
Lacerta	Lac	Lacertae
Leo	Leo	Leonis
Leo Minor	LMi	Leonis Minoris
Lepus	Lep	Leporis
Libra	Lib	Librae
Lupus	Lup	Lupi
Lynx	Lyn	Lyncis
Lyra	Lyr	Lyrae
Mensa	Men	Mensae
Microscopium	Mic	Microscopii
Monoceros	Mon	Monocerotis
Musca	Mus	Muscae
Norma	Nor	Normae
Octans	Oct	Octantis
Ophiuchus	Oph	Ophiuchi
Orion	Ori	Orionis
Pavo	Pav	Pavonis
Pegasus	Peg	Pegasi
Perseus	Per	Persei
Phoenix	Phe	Phocnicis
Pictor	Pic	Pictoris
Pisces	Psc	Piscium
Piscis Austrinus	PsA	Piscis Austrini
Puppis	Pup	Puppis
Pyxis	Pyx	Pyxidis
Reticulum	Ret	Reticuli

CONSTELLATION ABBREVIATIONS (*Continued*)

Name of constellation	Abbreviation	Genitive form of constellation
Sagitta...................	Sge	Sagittae
Sagittarius................	Sgr	Sagittarii
Scorpius..................	Sco	Scorpii
Sculptor..................	Scl	Sculptoris
Scutum...................	Sct	Scuti
Serpens...................	Ser	Serpentis
Sextans..................	Sex	Sextantis
Taurus...................	Tau	Tauri
Telescopium..............	Tel	Telescopii
Triangulum...............	Tri	Trianguli
Triangulum Australe........	TrA	Trianguli Australis
Tucana...................	Tuc	Tucanae
Ursa Major...............	UMa	Ursae Majoris
Ursa Minor...............	UMi	Ursae Minoris
Vela.....................	Vel	Velorum
Virgo....................	Vir	Virginis
Volans...................	Vol	Volantis
Vulpecula............	Vul	Vulpeculae

TABLE FOR CONVERSION OF DECIMAL OF DAY TO HOURS AND MINUTES*

Decimal of day	0.00	0.01	0.02	0.03	0.04	0.05	0.06	0.07	0.08	0.09	Decimal of day
0.00	0h 0m	0h 14m	0h 29m	0h 43m	0h 58m	1h 12m	1h 26m	1h 41m	1h 55m	2h 10m	0.00
0.10	2 24	2 38	2 53	3 7	3 22	3 36	3 50	4 5	4 19	4 34	0.10
0.20	4 48	5 2	5 17	5 31	5 46	6 0	6 14	6 29	6 43	6 58	0.20
0.30	7 12	7 26	7 41	7 55	8 10	8 24	8 38	8 53	9 7	9 22	0.30
0.40	9 36	9 50	10 5	10 19	10 34	10 48	11 2	11 17	11 31	11 46	0.40
0.50	12 00	12 14	12 29	12 43	12 58	13 12	13 26	13 41	13 55	14 10	0.50
0.60	14 24	14 38	14 53	15 7	15 22	15 36	15 50	16 5	16 19	16 34	0.60
0.70	16 48	17 2	17 17	17 31	17 46	18 0	18 14	18 29	18 43	18 58	0.70
0.80	19 12	19 26	19 41	19 55	20 10	20 24	20 38	20 53	21 7	21 22	0.80
0.90	21 36	21 50	22 5	22 19	22 34	22 48	23 2	23 17	23 31	23 46	0.90
Decimal of day	0.00	0.01	0.02	0.03	0.04	0.05	0.06	0.07	0.08	0.09	Decimal of day

* By interpolation the decimal of a day to thousandths may be obtained thus:

$$5^h\ 24^m = 0^d.225 \qquad 15^h\ 42^m = 0^d.654$$
$$10\ 30 = 0.437 \qquad 20\ 54 = 0.871$$

Also:

$$0^d.1 = 2^h\ 2.4^m\ 0^s$$
$$0.01 = 0\ 14\ 24$$
$$0.001 = 0\ 1\ 26.4$$
$$0.0001 = 0\ 0\ 8.64$$

JULIAN DAY TABLE 1940–1950*

Year / Month	1940	1941	1942	1943	1944	1945	1946	1947	1948	1949	1950
January	29629	29995	30360	30725	31090	31456	31821	32186	32551	32917	33282
February	29660	30026	30391	30756	31121	31487	31852	32217	32582	32948	33313
March	29689	30054	30419	30784	31150	31515	31880	32245	32611	32976	33341
April	29720	30085	30450	30815	31181	31546	31911	32276	32642	33007	33372
May	29750	30115	30480	30845	31211	31576	31941	32306	32672	33037	33402
June	29781	30146	30511	30876	31242	31607	31972	32337	32703	33068	33433
July	29811	30176	30541	30906	31272	31637	32002	32367	32733	33098	33463
August	29842	30207	30572	30937	31303	31668	32033	32398	32764	33129	33494
September	29873	30238	30603	30968	31334	31699	32064	32429	32795	33160	33525
October	29903	30268	30633	30998	31364	31729	32094	32459	32825	33190	33555
November	29934	30299	30664	31029	31395	31760	32125	32490	32856	33221	33586
December	29964	30329	30694	31059	31425	31790	32155	32520	32886	33251	33616

* 2,400,000 plus the value given in the table is the Julian Day for the zero day of each month. To find the Julian Day for a given date, add the day of the month for that year to the figures under the respective month and year; thus January 15, 1940 = 2429629 plus 15 = J.D. 2429644; December 25, 1950 = 2433616 plus 25 = J.D. 2433641.

SOME INTERESTING VARIABLE STARS

Name	R.A. Decl.: 1900		Magnitude		Period	Remarks
			Max.	Min.		
γ Cassiopeiae................	00ʰ 51ᵐ	+60°.2	1.6	2.9	Irr.	Erratic
o Ceti......................	02 14	−03.4	3.4†	9.2†	331ᵈ	Mira
β Persei....................	03 02	+40.6	2.4	3.5	2.867	Algol
ζ Aurigae...................	04 55	+40.9	4.9*	5.6*	972.	Eclipsing
ε Aurigae...................	04 55	+43.7	3.3	4.1	9900.	Eclipsing
α Orionis...................	05 50	+07.4	0.5	1.1	2070.?	Red Irregular
L₂ Puppis...................	07 10	−44.5	3.1†	6.3†	140.	Long-period
R Carinae...................	09 30	−62.3	4.4†	9.4†	309.	Long-period
l Carinae...................	09 42	−62.0	3.6	4.8	35.5	Cepheid
R Hydrae...................	13 24	−22.8	4.2†	9.5†	405.	Variable period
R Coronae Borealis........	15 44	+28.5	5.9	15.0	Irr.	Erratic
R Scuti.....................	18 42	−05.8	4.5	9.0	145.	Variable range
β Lyrae.....................	18 46	+33.2	3.4	4.1	12.908	Eclipsing
κ Pavonis...................	18 47	−67.4	3.8	5.2	9.09	Cepheid
η Aquilae...................	19 47	+00.7	3.8	4.5	7.176	Cepheid
χ Cygni.....................	19 47	+32.7	5.1†	13.3†	407.	Long-period
SS Cygni....................	21 39	+43.1	8.2	12.0	50.4	U Geminorum
μ Cephei....................	21 40	+58.3	3.7	4.7	Irr.	Red Irregular
δ Cephei....................	22 25	+57.9	3.6	4.2	5.366	Cepheid
R Aquarii...................	23 39	−15.8	6.4†	10.3†	387.	Peculiar Long-period

* *Photographic magnitudes; all others visual.* † *Mean magnitude.*

REMARKABLE NOVAE

Name	Year max.	Discoverer	Position, 1900	Max. mag.	Present mag.	Remarks
B Cassiopeiae	1572	Schuler	$00^h\ 19^m\ +63°6$	-4	16?	Tycho's Nova (Super)
Nova Ophiuchi	1604	Brunowski	17 24 $+21.4$	-2	14?	Kepler's Nova (Super)
Nova Vulpeculae	1670	Anthleme	19 43 $+27.1$	3	16	
T Coronae Borealis	1866	Birmingham	15 55 $+26.2$	2	10	Possible Recurring Nova
Q Cygni	1876	Schmidt	21 38 $+42.4$	3	15	
T Aurigae	1891	Anderson	05 25 $+30.4$	4	15	
RS Ophiuchi	{ 1898 { 1933	Fleming } Loreta }	17 45 -06.7	4	11–12	Recurring Nova
Nova Persei	1901	Anderson	03 24 $+43.6$	0	12–14	Oscillations at minimum
Nova Geminorum	1912	Enebo	06 48 $+32.3$	3	14	
Nova Aquilae	1918	Bower	18 44 $+00.5$	-1	11	
Nova Cygni	1920	Denning	19 56 $+53.3$	2	15	
RR Pictoris	1925	Watson	06 35 -62.6	1	10	Still fading
DQ Herculis	1934	Prentice	18 05 $+45.8$	1	11	Still fading
Nova Lacertae	1936	Gomi	22 12 $+55.1$	2	14	

INDEX

References to figures are given by the number of the figure in italics

A

A.A.V.S.O., 21, *33*
Absolute magnitude, 209
Adams, W. S., 154
Algol, 59
  period, 193
  variables, *177*, 179, 182, 194
Al-Sufi, 21
American Association of Variable
  Star Observers, 32, 33, *33*
Anderson, T. D., 122, 218
Andromeda
  γ, 174
  nebula, *129*
    distance, 75
    novae, 130
  nova, magnitude, 130
  RX, 59, *156*
  S (nova), 61
  W, curve, *160*
  Z, 61, 159, *160*
  ζ, 61, 182
Angström, 206
Antares, 91, 207
Anthleme, 218
Apsidal motion, *190*, 191
Aquarius
  CY, 65, *67*
  nebulosity, *112*
  R, *111*, 113, 217

Aquila
  DO, (nova), *127*, 128
  EL, (nova), 125, *126*
  η, 5, 63, 67
  nova (1918), 124, *126*, 128, 132, 218
  R, 100
  UU, 152, 153
  V356 (nova), 138
  V368 (nova), *126*
  V386 (nova), *127*
Arcturus, 20, 207
Argelander, F. G. A., 13, 21, 22, 26
Aries
  RV, *67*
  RW, *67*
Astronomische Gesellschaft, 17
Atlases
  A.A.V.S.O., 21
  BD., *22*, 23
  Beyer-Graff, 23
  Cordoba, 23
  Kleine, 21
  Norton, 21
  Santiago, 23
  Schurig, 21
  Upton, 21
  Uranametria Nova, 21
Atom, 203
Auriga
  ε, 175, 180, 195, 196
  RW, 168

Auriga, S, 108
SS, 150, *150*, 152
T (nova), 125, 132, *218*
TU, *116*
TX, 116
UW, 116
UY, 168
ζ, 175, 195, 196

B

Baade, W., 146
Bailey, S. I., 15, 35
Balazs, J., 69
Barnard, E. E., 138
Bayer, J., 21
BD. −8°4352, 174
Berman, L., 163
Beta Canis Majoris Stars, 85
Beta Lyrae stars, *177*, 179, 182, 194
Biermann, 142
Birmingham, 218
Blazhko, S. N., 186
Bond, G. P., 15
Bootes
γ, 86
RY, 168
Bowen, I. S., 135
Bower, G. N., 218
British Astronomical Association, 32
Brunowski, 218
Burwell, C. G., 170

C

Camelopardalis
R, 61, *110*
RU, 119
RY, 117
S, 61, 109, *109*, 208
U, 117
X, *96*, *99*
Z, 61

Cancer
SY, 168
Canes Major
β, 61
Cannon, A. J., 13, 16
Capella, 91, 207
Carina
CS, *67*
DW, 179
η, 158, *159*, 165
GL, *191*
l, 85, 217
R, 217
U, *67*
Cassiopeia
B (nova), 218
γ, 61, 169, *170*, 217
RW, *67*
RX, *67*
T, *96*
TU, *67*
VX, 166
XX, 194
Catalogues, 13, 20, 21
Centaurus
δ, *67*
ω, 84
R, 111, *111*
RR, 61
SV, 193
SX, 89
Cepheids
light curves, 66, *67*
measuring rods, 199
period-luminosity, 71
physical conditions, 77
spectra, 78
temperature, 78, 101
Cepheus
δ, 5, 25, 59, 60, 61
μ, 118, 217
T, *96*
U, 193
VV, 195, 196

Cepheus, VW, 192
  X, *97*
  YZ, 166
Cetus
  constellation, *3*
  omicron, 2, 16, 49, 21
Chandler, S. C., 13, 193
Constellations, 212
Corona Austrina, 165
  AQ, *67*
  BQ, *67*
  DE, *67*
  R, 166
  Borealis
    R, 1, 6, 59, 60, *162*, 163, 217
    T, *126*, 218
Crab Nebula, 141, *141*
Crux
  W, 179
Cygnus
  AF, 114, *115*
  α, 133
  β, 174
  BF, 170
  χ, 16, 52, 94, 98, 102, *110*, 217
  DF, 89
  DT, *67*
  Nova (1920), 67, 125, *126*, 138
  P (nova), 171
  Q (nova), 218
  R, *24*, 25
  SS, 17, 61, 151, 152, *153*, 217
  WW, 182
  X, 67
  Y, 190, 194

D

Darkening at the limb, 182, 183
Decimal of day, 215
Delphinus
  V, *98*
Denning, W. F., 218
Detre, L., 69

Doppler, C., 79, 175
Doppler effect, 208
Doradus
  β, 17
  RW, 194
Draco
  RW, 69
Dugan, R. S., 35, 186, 193
Duncan, J. C., 141

E

Eclipsing binaries
  amplitudes, 180
  apsidal motion, 190, *191*
  darkening at the limb, 182, *183*
  eccentric orbits, 188, *189*
  ellipticity, *178*
  exceptional systems, 194
  light curves, 176, *177*
  physical elements, 186
  radial velocities, 184, *185*
  reflection effect, 184
  types, 179
Eddington, A. S., 80, 81, 83, 108
Elvey, C. T., 47, 154, 157
Enebo, S., 218
Erratic variables, 161

F

Fabricius, D., 2
Fetlaar, J., 186
Finsen, W. S., 138
Flamsteed, J., 21
Fleming, W. P., 64, 218

G

Gaposchkin, S., 60, 101
Gemini
  η, 59, 118
  Nova (1912), 218

Gemini, R, 208
    S, *93*, 94
    T, *93*, 94
    U, 6, 59, 60, 150, *151*
    W, 66, *67*
    YY, 194
    ζ, 59
Globular cluster, 14
Gomi, K., 218
Goodricke, J. G., 5, 62
Graff, K., 23, 59
Greek alphabet, 211
Guthnick, P., 59

H

Hagen, J. G., 26
Hartwig, E., 13, 186, 193
Heiss, E., 26
Hercules
    α, 6, 174
    AH, 158
    AR, 69, *70*
    DQ, (nova), 67, 125, *126*, 132,
        138, 159, 174
    RS, *96*
    S, 100
    SX, 119
    T, *99*
Herschel, J. F. W., 6, 23
Hertzsprung, E., 66, 73, 74
Hipparchus, 20, 121
Hoffmeister, C., 12
Holwarda, 3
Hubble, E. P., 75, 130
Huffer, C. M., 120
Hydra
    R, 5, 16, 99, *100*, 217
    T, 93, 94, *96*
    V, 117, *117*

J

Joy, A. H., 102, 154
Julian day calendar, 29

K

Kapteyn, J. C., 23
Keplar, J., 122, 188
Kirch, G., 5
Kirchhoff, G. R., 205
Klein, H. J., 21
Kopal, Z., 186
Krat, W., 186
Kuiper, G. P., 131, 138, 174
Kukarkin, B. W., 76, 155, 156

L

Lacerta
    CP (nova), *126*, 134, *148*, 218
    RT, *185*
    SW, 192
    Z, *67*
Leavitt, H., 16, 71, *72*, 74
Leo
    R, 52, 101
    S, 16
    X, 152
Leo Minor
    Y, 69
Lepus
    R, 61
Light equation, 56
Loreta, E., 143, 218
Ludendorff, H., 60, 66
Luyten, W. J., 131
Lynx
    RW, 92
Lyra
    AY, 152
    β, 3, 60, 61, 67
    nebula, *137*
    RR, 59, 60, 61, 64, 69, 85

M

Magellanic clouds, *15*, 17, *72*, 75
Magnitudes, 18, *19*

Maraldi, G., 5
Martin, E. G., 71
Mayall, M. W., 11, 93
Mayall, N. U., 141
McLaughlin, D. B., 170
Menzel, D. H., 135, 137, 154
Merrill, P. W., 103, 113, 170
Meyers, E. J., 186
Michelson, A. A., 118
Minkowski, R., 149
Mira Ceti stars, 59, 60, 93, 94, 97,
      98, 100, 101, 103, 104, 106,
      107
Monoceros
  R, 166
  RU, 190
  U, *89*
  VW, *167*
  X, *115*
Montanari, G., 3
Moon, 20
Müller, G., 13
Musca
  RT, *67*
  S, *67*

N

Nebular variables, 165
Nicholson, S. B., 102
Nijland, A. A., 27, 59
Norma
  U, *67*
  UX, *67*
Norton, A. P., 21
Nova
  curves, *126*
  Cygni (1920), *126*
  DQ Herculis (1934), *134*
  (1572), 147
  luminosity, 130
  occurrence, 128
  physics, 132
  range, 144

Nova, recurrence, 143
  rise to maximum, 145
  (1604), 147
  types, 124
Nova-like variables, 158

O

O'Keefe, J., 163
Olcott, W. T., *32*
Ophiuchus
  Nova (1604), 122, *148*, **218**
  Nova (1919), 138
  RS, (nova), 61, *126*, 143, 155,
    218
  V, 93, 94, *109*
Orion
  α, 118, 159, 217
  BN, 166
  CN, 157, *157*, 158
  CO, 168
  constellation, *20*
  FU (nova), 168
  nebula, 15
  RY, 168
  T, 15, 61, *165*
  UX, 168

P

Pannekock, A., 186
Parenago, P. P., 155, 156
Payne-Gaposchkin, C., 60, 81, 101, 149,
    160
Pavo
  κ, 217
Pease, F. G., 118
Pegasus
  AU, 67
  BP, 179
  CW, 182
  RU, 152, 153
  TW, 115
Peltier, L. C., 143, *143*

Perseus
  AX, 61
  b, 182
  β, 3, 4, *4*, 5, 16, 61, 179, 217
  Nova (1901), 122, 123, *126*, 132, 138, 218
  φ, 170
  RT, 192
  S, 117
  TT, *116*
  TZ, 157
  U, 41, 42, *42*
  UZ, 115
  VX, 67, *67*
  X, 170
  Y, 108
Pettit, E., 102
Photographic estimations, 38
  methods, 34
Pickering, E. C., frontispiece, 23, 26, 35, 58, 63, 123, 186
Pictor
  RR (nova), *8*, *127*, 132, 138, 218
Pigott, 13, 62
Pisces
  #19, 208
Pleiades, 165
Polaris, 1, 169
Prager, R., 13, 57, 70
Prentice, J. P. M., 218
Procyon, 207
Ptolemy, 20, 21
Puppis
  AD, *67*
  L₂, 217
  W, 92
  X, *67*
  ζ, 208
Purkyně effect, 36, 37
Pyxis
  T (nova), 145

R

R Coronae Borealis stars, 161
Reflection effect, 184
Rigel, 207
Ritter, W. McK., 80
Roberts, A. W., 186
Rodinger, 186
Roemer, O., 57
Ross, E. E., 17
RR Tauri stars, 167
RV Tauri stars, 87
Russell, H. N., 35, 186, 192

S

Sagitta
  R, 59, 89, *89*
  S, 59, *67*
  U, 194
  V, 160
Sagittarius
  RY, 61, 164
  V467, *67*
  V527, *67*
  V732, *126*
  W, *82*
  WZ, *67*
  YZ, *67*
Santiago Observatory, 23
Scaliger, J., 29
Schmidt, J., 26, 218
Schneller, H., 13
Schoenfeld, E., 13, 22, 26
Schuler, 218
Schurig, R., 21
Schwarzschild, M., 82, 83, 108
Scorpius
  α, 118
  U (nova), *126*, 144, 155
  Z, 94
Scott, R. W., 107
Scutum
  R, 5, 59, *89*, 90, 119

Serpens
    RT (nova), *127*, 128
Shapley, H., 35, 74, *74*, 147
Siedentopf, H., 81
Sirius, 20, 101, 132, 207
Sitterly, B. W., 186
Spectroscope, 204
Spectroscopic binaries, 175
Stebbins, J., 120, 186
Stellar spectra, 207
Sterne, T. E., 117, 192
Stuker, P., 23
Sun, 18, 83, 147, *183*, 207
Super nova
    frequency, 148
    in Canes Venatici, 147
      IC 4182, *148*
      NGC 1003, *146*
        3184, 149
        4321, 149
        6946, 149
    of 1572, *148*
      1604, *148*
    S Andromedae, 145
    spectra, 149
Swope, H. H., 191

T

Taurus
    RR, 60, 167, *168*
    RV, 59, 87, *88*
    RY, 166
    SZ, *67*
    XX, 125, *126*
Telescopes
    reflecting, *30*
    refracting, *31*
Triangulum
    R, *99*
Turner, H. H., 117
Tycho, Brahe, 21

U

U Geminorum stars, 149, 154, 155
Ulugh Beigh, 21
Unsold, A., 142
Upton, W., 21
Uranometria Nova, 21
Ursa Major
    β, 86
    ϵ, 86
    R, *97*
    RS, *97*
    S, 42, 43, 44, *45*
    SU, 151, *151*
    UX, 180, 194, 196, 197
    W, 61
    Z, *115*
    ζ, *175*
    Minor
      V, 61, *115*

V

Van den Bos, W. H., 138
Variables
    definition, 1
    derivation of maximum, 47
      period, 50
    discovery, 5, 6, 7, *7*, 9, *10*, 11, 12,
      12, 13
    estimations, 23
    kinds, 57
    nomenclature, 16
    red, 199
Vega, 20, 91
Venus, 2, 20
Virgo
    RU, 109
    T, 16, 86
    W, *87*, 119
    XX, *67*
Vulpecula
    Nova, 218
    SV, 65, *67*

Vulpecula, T, *67*
   U, 53, 54, *54*, 55, 56
   V, 89, *89*
   WW, 166

W

W Ursae Majoris stars, *177*, 179, 180, 181, 194.
W Virginis stars, 87
Wachmann, A. A., 17
Watson, R., 218
Webb, H. B., 23

Wendell, O. C., 35, 53
Whipple, F. L., 11, 149
Wright, F. W., 193
Wyse, A. B., 186

Z

Z Camelopardalis stars, 156, 157
Zanstra, H., 157
Zessewitch, W., 186
Zoellner, J. C. F., 35
Zwicky, F., 146, 148